MODERN KID PRESS

Second Grade Reading Comprehension Workbook

Silly Stories

THIS BOOK BELONGS TO:

Want free goodies?!

Email us at

modernkidpress@gmail.com

Title the email
"Reading Comprehension Grade 2"
and we'll send some goodies your way!

Follow us on
Instagram!
@modernkidpress

Questions & Customer Service:
Email us at modernkidpress@gmail.com!

Silly Stories: Second Grade Reading Comprehension Workbook

Written, illustrated, and cover design by Jacy Corral.

Table of Contents

Dear Caregiver,

Welcome to an exciting journey into the world of reading comprehension with *"Silly Stories: Second Grade Reading Comprehension Workbook!"* We are thrilled to have your child join us in developing their reading skills and fostering a love for reading. With this workbook, we aim to support your child's growth in key areas of reading comprehension while making it fun and enjoyable.

Throughout the workbook, we will be focusing on important reading comprehension skills that will help your child become a confident and engaged reader. From phonics and word recognition to understanding different types of texts, we've got it covered!

But here's a little secret: this workbook isn't just for your second grader! We've included a special section just for you, the caregiver, to brush up on your own reading skills. (Let's be honest, it's been a while since you were in second grade. Add to that the changes in how our kids are learning!) This is a fun way for you to join in and show your child that reading is important to the whole family.

To emphasize how important we believe FUN is to learning, we've included interactive activities, puzzles, and exercises to keep your child engaged while reinforcing their reading comprehension skills. There's nothing more rewarding than seeing your child light up when they understand and connect with what they're reading.

We encourage you to explore the workbook together with your child, engage in discussions about the texts, and celebrate their progress along the way. Remember, reading is a lifelong adventure, and your support and involvement make all the difference.

Thank you for partnering with us on this exciting reading comprehension journey. We're confident that together we can inspire a lifelong love for reading in your child.

Happy reading!

Sincerely,
The Modern Kid Press Team

MKP | Framework for Learning

At Modern Kid Press, we approach learning like building a house.

It involves having the right tools, preparing a strong foundation, practicing your skills, reviewing your progress, and ultimately achieving mastery. Just like a well-constructed house, this framework aims to support your child's learning journey by providing structure and a clear path towards success.

We believe that learning is best achieved through fun and enjoyment that engages young learners' minds and imaginations. That's why so many of our learning resources are funny, silly, and downright ridiculous! We hope your child will enjoy learning this material as much as we did creating it.

Tools

Mastery

MKP Framework for Learning

Preparation

Review

Practice

Key Reading Comprehension

SKILLS

Phonics and Word Recognition: Help your second grader become a word detective! They'll learn how to figure out words by using letter sounds and recognizing common words they see a lot.

Reading Fluency: Watch your second grader's reading skills soar! They'll practice reading smoothly, at the right speed, and with expression, so it sounds like they're telling a story.

Vocabulary: Let's unlock new words together! Your second grader will discover how to understand tricky words by looking at the clues in the sentences. And they'll have fun using those words in their own writing!

Comprehension: Dive into the world of reading! Your second grader will learn to understand stories and information by asking questions, telling what happened in the story, and connecting different books they've read.

Text Types and Purposes: Explore all kinds of reading! From exciting stories to cool facts, your second grader will learn how to read and understand different types of texts, like poems, stories, and informational books.

Informational Text: Let's become expert readers of non-fiction! Your second grader will learn how to understand and analyze all those cool facts in books and articles, like in science or history.

Literary Text: Step into the world of stories and poems! Your second grader will learn about characters, settings, and plots, and discover the magic of literary texts.

Critical Thinking: Get ready for some brain power! Your second grader will use their thinking skills to figure out tricky parts, make guesses, and put all the pieces together to understand what they're reading.

Look for this ribbon on each story listing the corresponding Common Core standards. An explanation of each standard can be found on page 94.

Tools for

 **CAREGIVERS**

This section is for the parents and caregivers out there! Before your child jumps into the learning sections of this book, read through the following pages. These tools will equip you to support your child's learning and help them to improve their reading comprehension skills. Your child will be introduced to each tool as "reading skills" within the introduction of each section. If they need help with their practice pages, feel free to flip back to these tools for a refresher on different ways to help them get the most out of their reading experience.

But first...

Why is reading comprehension so important?

Second grade is a crucial year for developing reading comprehension skills, which are essential for becoming a successful reader in the long term. During this year, students typically transition from learning to read to reading to learn. Specifically, they start using their reading skills to gain knowledge and learn new information across all subjects, including math, science, and social studies.

A strong foundation in reading comprehension skills at this stage is critical because it helps students to understand and retain what they read. They learn to make connections between different texts and topics. They also develop critical thinking and analysis skills. These skills become increasingly important as students progress through the grades, and they become more complex and demanding.

Students who need help with reading comprehension in second grade may find it challenging to keep up with the curriculum in later grades. Therefore, second graders must receive targeted instruction and practice in reading comprehension skills to ensure that they become proficient readers who are well-equipped to succeed academically and beyond.

Bring on the tools!

Let's face it: a lot has changed since most of us parents and caregivers were in school. It's time to clear out the cobwebs and brush up on some of the learning strategies that have changed since those days. Here are several tools you can use to help your second grader improve their reading comprehension:

Retelling

Have your child read a short story, then have them retell it in their own words. This activity will help them practice summarizing and identifying the main idea and supporting details.

Here's how retelling helps second graders improve their reading comprehension:

1. **Understanding the Text:** Retelling requires students to recall what they have read, which helps them understand the text better. When they retell the story in their own words, they process the information and connect it to their prior knowledge, which enhances their comprehension.

2. **Identifying Important Details:** Retelling helps students identify important details of the story. They need to recall and organize the main events, characters, and settings, which requires them to focus on the critical elements of the text.

3. **Developing Oral Language Skills:** Retelling helps students develop their oral language skills, including vocabulary, sentence structure, and syntax. When they retell a story, they practice using descriptive words and constructing coherent sentences, which helps them express their thoughts more effectively.

4. **Enhancing Memory:** Retelling can improve students' memory by encouraging them to recall and retain the information from the text. This kind of practice helps them remember the story and its details, which can contribute to their long-term comprehension.

5. **Fostering Critical Thinking:** Retelling can also promote critical thinking skills, as students must analyze the text, make connections, and draw conclusions. Telling you the story in their own words helps them become more thoughtful readers and better understand its meaning.

Sequencing

Give your child a set of pictures or events from a story and have them put them in the correct order. This activity will help them practice identifying the sequence of events in their reading.

Here's how sequencing helps second graders improve their reading comprehension:

1. **Understanding the Text:** Sequencing requires students to identify and organize the events in a story, which helps them understand the text better. When they sequence the story, they process the information and connect it to their prior knowledge, which enhances their comprehension.

2. **Identifying Cause and Effect:** Sequencing helps students identify the cause-and-effect relationship between the events in the story. They need to recognize which events happened first, second, and so on, which allows them to understand how each event led to the next.

3. **Developing Critical Thinking Skills:** Sequencing helps students develop critical thinking skills, as they must analyze the story, make connections, and draw conclusions. This activity helps them become more thoughtful readers and better understand the story's meaning.

4. **Improving Memory:** Sequencing can improve students' memory by encouraging them to recall and retain the information from the text. This kind of practice helps them remember the story and its details, which can contribute to their long-term comprehension.

5. **Enhancing Oral Language Skills:** Sequencing can also improve students' oral language skills by encouraging them to use transition words such as "first," "next," and "finally." This helps them organize their thoughts and communicate their ideas more effectively.

Making Connections

Have your child read a story and connect it to their own lives or experiences. This activity will help them understand how stories relate to their experiences and build their background knowledge.

Here's how making connections helps second graders improve their reading comprehension:

1. **Activating Prior Knowledge:** Making connections requires students to activate their prior knowledge by connecting what they already know to what they are reading. This connection helps them make sense of the text and creates a foundation for further comprehension.

2. **Developing Vocabulary:** Making connections can help students build vocabulary skills by connecting new words to words and concepts they already know. This practice allows them to better understand and retain the new vocabulary.

3. **Improving Comprehension:** Making connections can improve students' comprehension by helping them understand the story more deeply. By connecting the text to their own lives and experiences, students can better relate to and understand the story.

4. **Enhancing Critical Thinking:** Making connections can also improve critical thinking skills, as students must analyze and connect the text to their own lives and experiences. This helps them become more thoughtful readers and understand the story's meaning better.

5. **Building Empathy:** Making connections can also help students develop empathy by connecting the text to their personal experiences and feelings. In doing so, they can better understand the characters and their motivations, which can contribute to a deeper comprehension of the story.

Questioning

Have the students generate questions about a story before, during, and after reading. Practicing asking questions can help students clarify their understanding of the text.

Here's how questioning helps second graders improve their reading comprehension:

1. **Encouraging Active Reading:** Questioning encourages students to read actively by asking them to think about the text and generate their own questions. This helps them stay engaged with the text and fosters a deeper understanding.

2. **Developing Critical Thinking Skills:** Questioning helps students develop critical thinking skills by asking them to analyze the text and generate their own ideas. This helps them become more thoughtful readers and understand the story's meaning better.

3. **Improving Comprehension:** Questioning can improve students' comprehension by encouraging them to actively think about the text and connect it to their experiences. This practice helps them understand the story more deeply and can contribute to a richer comprehension.

4. **Identifying Main Ideas:** Questioning can help students identify the text's main ideas by asking them to focus on key details and concepts. Finding the main ideas helps them understand the story's overall message and how each part fits together.

5. **Encouraging Reflection:** Questioning encourages students to reflect on what they have read by asking them to generate their own questions and ideas. Doing so helps students develop metacognitive skills, allowing them to achieve an even deeper understanding of the text.

Visualizing

Have your child listen to a story and then draw a picture of what they visualize in their minds. This will help them build their comprehension by creating mental images of the text.

Here's how visualizing, or creating mental images of the text, helps second graders improve their reading comprehension:

1. **Encouraging Active Reading:** Visualizing encourages students to read actively by engaging their imagination and creating mental images of the text. This helps them stay engaged with the text and fosters a deeper understanding.

2. **Developing Comprehension Skills:** Visualizing can improve students' comprehension by helping them create a mental map of the story and its characters. This practice can help them better understand the plot, characters, and setting and can contribute to a richer comprehension.

3. **Improving Vocabulary:** Visualizing can improve students' vocabulary skills by helping them connect new words to their mental images of the text. Doing so can help them better understand and remember new vocabulary.

4. **Encouraging Inference:** Visualizing encourages students to make inferences by using the details in the text to create a mental image. This helps them develop their inferential skills and better draw conclusions based on the text.

5. **Enhancing Creativity:** Visualizing encourages students to use their creativity by imagining what the story and its characters look like. Creating those mental images can help them develop their imagination and creativity, which can contribute to a deeper understanding of the text.

Section 1

 ## LITERARY TEXTS

A literary text is a written work that is considered to have artistic or literary merit. It often contains creative or imaginative language, and may have themes or symbols that convey deeper meaning. Examples of literary texts include novels, short stories, poems, and plays.

Studying literary texts is an important part of the second grade curriculum and helps develop reading comprehension, critical thinking, and language skills.

Reading Skills

Before you jump into the full stories in this section, brush up on your reading skills with the activities on the following pages.

 Predict

 Retell the Story

 Read Aloud

 Consider the Character's Point of View

 Make Connections

 Stop and Ask Questions

 Discuss the Author's Purpose

 Visualize

Come back to this page and color in the stars after you finish each activity!

Section 1: Literary Texts

 # Reading Skill: Predict

Friends in the City

Take a look at the title and illustrations for this story. What do you think the story might be about?

_____

_____

Once upon a time, in the bustling city of New York, a monkey named Max was swinging through Central Park when he spotted a tiny squirrel named Sammy perched on a tree branch. Sammy looked lonely, so Max decided to introduce himself.

Let's update your predictions. What do you think the story is about now? What do you think might happen? What changes might you make to your original predictions?

_____

_____

"Hi there! I'm Max. What's your name?" asked the friendly monkey.

The squirrel looked up and was surprised to see a monkey talking to him. "I'm Sammy," he replied shyly.

Max and Sammy quickly became friends and started hanging out in the park every day. They would share acorns and tell each other stories. One day, they overheard a group of birds talking about a mysterious island in the middle of the lake in Central Park. The island was said to be home to a hidden treasure that could only be found by solving a riddle.

What do you think will happen next? Which of your predictions need to be updated based on what you know now?

_____

_____

Max and Sammy were intrigued by the idea of a treasure hunt and decided to embark on an adventure to find it. They worked together to solve the riddle, which led them on a wild goose chase around the park. They had to jump over fallen branches, climb trees, and even swing from vines to get to the island.

What do you think will happen next? What evidence can you find to support your prediction?

_____

_____

Finally, they arrived at the island and found the treasure hidden inside a hollow tree. It was a small chest filled with shiny jewels and gold coins. Max and Sammy were overjoyed and decided to split the treasure equally between them.

As they made their way back to their treehouse in the park, they realized that the true treasure was their friendship and the adventures they had together.

How did you do? Look back at your predictions. Were they accurate? Did your predictions change as you read the text? What evidence from the text did you use to support your predictions?

_____

_____

Reading Skill: Read Aloud

Read the following story out loud to a friend or grown up:

Lucy's Messy Day

Lucy was a fluffy white poodle who loved to run and play in the park. Her favorite activity was chasing squirrels up trees, but one day she got a little too close and fell into a muddy puddle. She was so embarrassed and sad that she ran away from the park and hid under a tree. But then, her owner came looking for her, found her, and took her home to give her a warm bath and some treats. From that day on, Lucy learned to be more careful and not let her accidents bring her down.

Answer the following questions:

Who is the main character of the story? _____

What is the setting of the story? _____

What happened at the beginning of the story? What is the problem?

_____

_____

What happened in the middle of the story? How does the character work to solve the problem?

_____

_____

What happened at the end of the story? How was the problem resolved?

_____

_____

Reading Skill: Make Connections

Read the following story:

Lila Feels Left Out

Lila was in second grade, and she loved her friends. She would play with them during recess, share her snacks, and always be there to help them. One day, Lila overheard her classmates talking about a birthday party that one of them was having. Lila waited eagerly for an invitation, but it never came.

The next day, Lila tried to talk to her friends about the party, but they all seemed to be ignoring her. She felt left out and hurt. Lila wondered if she had done something wrong. Was she not a good enough friend?

Lila went to her teacher to ask if she could talk to her. The teacher saw how sad Lila was and asked her what was wrong. Lila explained that she wasn't invited to her friend's birthday party, and she didn't know why.

The teacher listened and comforted Lila. She told her that sometimes, people make mistakes, and it's important to forgive them and move on. She also reminded Lila that there are always people who care about her and want to be her friend.

With her teacher's help, Lila felt better. She decided to invite her classmates to a party of her own, where everyone could have fun and feel included. The next day at school, Lila handed out her invitations, and her classmates happily accepted. Lila learned that being kind and inclusive can make a big difference, and she was happy to have such great friends.

Answer the following questions:

In what ways do you feel similar to Lila?

_____

_____

_____

In what ways do you feel similar to Lila's teacher?

_____

_____

_____

In what ways do you feel similar to Lila's classmates?

_____

_____

_____

Do any of the events in the story remind you of things that have happened in your own life? Write about them here.

_____

_____

_____

_____

_____

_____

Reading Skill: Discuss the Author's Purpose

Read the following story:

The Tortoise and the Hare

The tortoise and the hare agreed to have a race. The hare, who was much faster than the tortoise, was so confident that he took a nap during the race. Meanwhile, the tortoise kept on moving slowly and steadily. The hare woke up and started running again, but he was too late. The tortoise had already crossed the finish line and won the race. The hare learned that overconfidence can lead to defeat, while persistence and consistency can lead to success.

Answer the following questions:

Why do you think the author wrote this story? _____

_____

What lesson does the author want the reader to learn? _____

_____

What lesson can be learned from this story? _____

_____

Reading Skill: Retell the Story

Read the following story:

Samantha's Special Balloon

Samantha held tightly to her favorite blue balloon as she walked through the park with her family. Suddenly, a strong gust of wind blew the balloon out of her hand and up into the sky. Samantha watched with tears in her eyes as the balloon floated away, becoming smaller and smaller until it was out of sight.

Feeling sad, Samantha's family tried to comfort her by suggesting they buy a new balloon. But Samantha knew it wouldn't be the same. She missed her old balloon, the one that had been with her through so many happy memories.

Days passed, and Samantha had nearly given up hope of ever seeing her balloon again. But then, something miraculous happened. As she was walking home from school, she spotted something blue in a nearby tree. It was her balloon! The wind had carried it all the way to this tree, and it had become tangled in the branches.

Samantha's face lit up with joy as she carefully untangled the balloon and held it close. It wasn't lost anymore; it was found. And Samantha knew that this balloon would be with her for many more happy memories to come.

Rewrite the story in your own words.

First... _____

_____

Next... _____

_____

Then... _____

_____

Finally... _____

_____

Reading Skill: Consider the Character's Point of View

Read the following story:

A Great Game for Max

It was the day of the big game, and Max felt the nervous butterflies fluttering in his stomach. He had been practicing for weeks, perfecting his moves and strategy, and now it was time to put it all to the test. Max was a soccer player, and today's game was the most important one of the season. He knew his team was counting on him to score goals and lead them to victory.

As the game started, Max felt his nerves calm down as he focused on the ball. He dribbled, passed, and weaved through the opposing team's defense, earning cheers and applause from the spectators. Max's hard work and dedication paid off when he scored the game-winning goal in the last minutes of the game. His team rushed to congratulate him, and Max couldn't help but feel a sense of pride and accomplishment. He knew that his big game was not just a success for him but for his team and all of their supporters.

Answer the following questions:

How does Max feel at the beginning of the game, and why? _____

_____

How does Max feel at the end of the game, and why? _____

_____

Why do Max's feelings change throughout the passage? _____

_____

Reading Skill: Stop and Ask Questions

Read the following story:

The Brave Unicorn and the Broken Horn

Once upon a time, in the magical land of Rainbowia, there lived a special unicorn named Sparkle. Sparkle had a beautiful mane that shimmered with all the colors of the rainbow. But there was something unique about Sparkle—unlike other unicorns, Sparkle had a broken horn.

Pause and think about what you just read.
Write one question you have about the text: _____

_____

One sunny day, Sparkle decided to explore the Enchanted Forest. As she trotted through the forest, she encountered a group of friendly woodland creatures. They gathered around Sparkle, curious about her broken horn. Squirrel chattered, "What happened to your horn, Sparkle?" Owl hooted, "How does it feel to have a broken horn?"

Pause and think about what you just read.
Write one question you have about the text: _____

_____

Sparkle paused and smiled, "Well, my friends, my horn may be broken, but that doesn't stop me from spreading joy and magic wherever I go." The woodland creatures were amazed by Sparkle's positive attitude. They realized that a broken horn couldn't diminish Sparkle's bravery and kindness.

Pause and think about what you just read.
Write one question you have about the text: _____

_____

As Sparkle continued her journey, she encountered a sparkling waterfall. She leaned closer to the water to take a drink and noticed her reflection. The broken horn reminded her of her inner strength and resilience. Sparkle realized that being different made her even more special.

Pause and think about what you just read.
What answers to your questions did you learn as you continued reading?

_____

_____

Section 1: Literary Texts

 Reading Skill: Visualize

The Magical Flying Pencil

Close your eyes and imagine a magical world with a pencil that can fly. Use your senses to create a mental image of the world.

Once upon a time, there was a pencil that could fly. It lived in a magical land where all objects had special powers. The pencil's power was to soar through the air and draw as it flew. It was owned by a young girl who loved to draw. She could create the most amazing pictures with her magical pencil.

How do you think the pencil is able to fly? _____

_____

What kinds of pictures do you think the girl draws? _____

_____

The pencil had special purple wings that were lighter than a butterfly's and faster than a hummingbird. One day, the girl drew a picture of a magnificent pair of wings that sparkled in the sun. To her surprise, the pencil gave the drawing a quick tap and the wings came to life! They even sprouted straps for the girl to slip onto her own arms. Now she could fly around with her special pencil!

What color do you think the girl's new wings are? _____

_____

What expression do you think the girl had on her face when the wings came to life?

_____

_____

From that day on, the girl and her pencil went on many adventures together, soaring through the skies and creating beautiful drawings wherever they went. People were amazed by the pencil's abilities and many wanted to own a magical pencil like hers.

What kinds of adventures do you think the girl and her pencil went on?

_____

_____

In the end, the girl realized that the pencil was too special to keep to herself, and she decided to share its magic with the world. She became an artist, using her pencil to create beautiful drawings that inspired others to imagine and dream. And the pencil continued to fly, bringing joy and wonder wherever it went.

> *Draw a picture of the story based on all of the things you imagined.*
> *Use colors and details that match your visualization of the story.*

Baylee and Jude were the best of friends. They loved playing together, exploring new places, and going on adventures. One sunny afternoon, while playing in the park, they stumbled upon a hidden entrance. It was small and looked like it was made out of candy. Baylee and Jude were curious, so they decided to investigate.

As they crawled through the candy entrance, they found themselves in a magical land made of junk food! The trees were made of lollipops, the grass was made of cotton candy, and the clouds were made of marshmallows. It was like nothing they had ever seen before.

Baylee and Jude started exploring the land, and soon they came across a giant chocolate cake. As they were about to take a bite, they heard a small voice. It was coming from the cake! They looked closer and saw that there were tiny people living inside the cake. The people were made of icing and candy, and they were scared. Baylee and Jude reassured them that they were there to help.

The two friends worked together to free the tiny people from the cake. They used their strength and teamwork to break the cake apart and rescue the icing people. When they were all free, the icing people were so grateful that they took Baylee and Jude on a tour of their magical land.

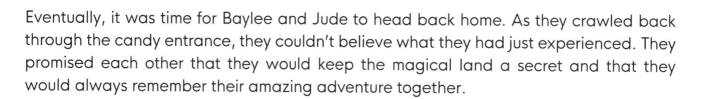

As they explored, Baylee and Jude learned about the different types of junk food that made up the land. They tasted chocolate rivers, candy canes, and licorice trees. It was the most delicious adventure they had ever been on.

Eventually, it was time for Baylee and Jude to head back home. As they crawled back through the candy entrance, they couldn't believe what they had just experienced. They promised each other that they would keep the magical land a secret and that they would always remember their amazing adventure together.

Reading Comprehension Questions

Question 1: What did Baylee and Jude find in the park?

[ ] a. A hidden entrance made of candy

[ ] b. A lost puppy

[ ] c. A secret garden

[ ] d. A treasure map

Question 2: What was the magical land made of?

[ ] a. Vegetables and fruit

[ ] b. Toys and games

[ ] c. Junk food

[ ] d. Flowers and plants

Question 3: What did Baylee and Jude find inside the giant chocolate cake?

[ ] a. A treasure map

[ ] b. Tiny people made of icing and candy

[ ] c. A magic wand

[ ] d. A lost puppy

Question 4: What did Baylee and Jude promise each other at the end of the story?

[ ] a. To keep the magical land a secret and to always remember their adventure together

[ ] b. To forget about the magical land and never speak of it again

[ ] c. To write a book about their adventure and become famous authors

[ ] d. To go back to the magical land and live there forever

For Fun! Draw your own magical land made of junk food.

Story 2: Rufus's Special Friend

RL.2.1
RL.2.3
RL.2.7

Rufus the dog loved to play outside in his yard. One day, he saw something unusual in the corner of the yard. It was a small robot, who had somehow ended up in Rufus's yard. At first, Rufus was scared of the robot and barked at it, but the robot didn't move. After a few minutes, Rufus realized that the robot wasn't dangerous and slowly approached it.

As Rufus got closer to the robot, he saw that it was actually a small toy robot that had lost its battery. Rufus picked up the robot in his mouth and brought it to his owner, who put in a new battery. The robot came to life and started to move, much to Rufus's delight. From that day on, Rufus and the robot were the best of friends, playing together in the yard every day.

Reading Comprehension Questions

Question 1: How did Rufus initially react to the robot in his yard?

[ ] a. He was happy

[ ] b. He was scared

[ ] c. He was confused

[ ] d. He ignored it

Question 2: What was wrong with the robot?

[ ] a. It was too big

[ ] b. It was too small

[ ] c. It was broken

[ ] d. It was too fast

Question 3: How did Rufus help the robot come to life?

[ ] a. He licked it

[ ] b. He picked it up

[ ] c. He hugged it

[ ] d. He talked to it

Question 4: What did Rufus and the robot do together?

[ ] a. Watch TV

[ ] b. Read books

[ ] c. Play in the yard

[ ] d. Take naps

Story 3: A Very Musical Unicorn

Once upon a time, in a magical forest, there lived a young unicorn named Twinkle. Twinkle loved music and dreamed of playing an instrument, but she wasn't sure which one to choose. One day, she stumbled upon a group of animals playing music together. She was mesmerized by the sound of a saxophone played by a friendly rabbit. From that moment, Twinkle knew that the saxophone was the instrument for her.

Twinkle started practicing on her own, but she found it challenging to play the saxophone with her hooves. She was about to give up when she met the rabbit who played the saxophone. The rabbit encouraged her to keep practicing and offered to teach her. Twinkle was thrilled and practiced every day with the rabbit's guidance.

As the weeks passed, Twinkle became better and better. She learned how to play songs and even wrote some of her own. She performed for her friends in the forest, and they were amazed by her talent.

Reading Comprehension Questions

Question 1: Who did Twinkle meet that encouraged her to keep practicing the saxophone?

_____

_____

_____

Question 2: What did Twinkle do every day to become better at playing the saxophone?

_____

_____

_____

Question 3: How did Twinkle's friends react to her performances?

_____

_____

_____

Question 4: Why was Twinkle hesitant to continue playing the saxophone at first?

_____

_____

_____

Story 4: Bubbles' Grand Adventure

RL.2.2
RL.2.3

A ticklish water bottle named Bubbles lived in a fridge with her friends, the leftover pizza and the carton of milk. Bubbles was always ticklish and would giggle uncontrollably whenever she was touched or bumped into. This made it difficult for her friends to take her out of the fridge without making a mess.

One day, Bubbles decided she wanted to see what was outside of the fridge. She asked her friends to help her, but they were afraid they would make her spill. Suddenly, the carton of milk had an idea. He suggested that they roll Bubbles out of the fridge slowly and carefully, so she wouldn't get too ticklish and start giggling.

The plan worked perfectly, and Bubbles was able to explore the kitchen without spilling a single drop. She even got to see the toaster and the blender, which she had only heard about before. From that day on, Bubbles was no longer afraid of leaving the fridge and would go on adventures with her friends whenever they could.

For Fun! Unscramble the words to reveal items found in the story:

S L E B B U B _____

E R O A T T S _____

T L E B O T _____

E G D I R F _____

Reading Comprehension Questions

Question 1: What is the name of the ticklish water bottle in the story?

_____

_____

_____

Question 2: Why was it difficult for Bubbles' friends to take her out of the fridge?

_____

_____

_____

Question 3: What was the carton of milk's idea to help Bubbles explore the kitchen without spilling?

_____

_____

_____

Question 4: Was Bubbles still afraid of leaving the fridge after her adventure with her friends?

_____

_____

_____

Story 5: Fish Need Friends, Too

Goldie was a goldfish who lived in a small tank in a little girl's room. She had everything she needed - food, water, and a cozy place to sleep. However, she often felt lonely because she didn't have any fish friends. Whenever the little girl's friends came over, they would always try to talk to her, but she could never understand them.

One day, the little girl brought home another goldfish named Fred. Goldie was excited to have a friend, but she was also a bit nervous. She had never shared her tank with another fish before. At first, they didn't get along very well. Fred liked to swim faster than Goldie, and she found it hard to keep up. But after a few days, they started to get along better. They even played a game where they would swim through the plastic plants together.

Despite their growing friendship, Goldie still felt a little left out when the little girl's friends came over. She could see them laughing and playing, but she couldn't join in. One day, she had an idea. She began to swim back and forth in front of the glass, making silly faces and wiggling her tail. To her surprise, the little girl's friends thought it was hilarious and began to tickle the tank, making Goldie giggle with delight.

Reading Comprehension Questions

Question 1: What did Goldie have trouble with?

_____

_____

_____

Question 2: How did Fred and Goldie start getting along?

_____

_____

_____

Question 3: How did Goldie feel when the little girl's friends came over?

_____

_____

_____

Question 4: How did Goldie make the little girl's friends laugh?

_____

_____

_____

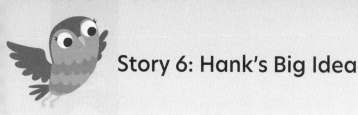

Story 6: Hank's Big Idea

Once there was a hippo named Hank who loved to throw parties. He would invite all of his animal friends to come and celebrate, but there was one problem. Whenever he got excited, he would sneeze confetti all over the place! At first, his friends thought it was funny, but after a while, they started to get annoyed.

Hank didn't know what to do. He loved to have fun and make people happy, but he didn't want to upset his friends. One day, he came up with an idea. He would invite everyone over for a confetti party! This way, he could sneeze all he wanted, and everyone would have a good time.

His friends were hesitant at first, but once they saw how much fun it was to play in confetti, they couldn't help but join in. Hank was so happy to see his friends having a good time, and he promised to only have confetti parties from now on.

Reading Comprehension Questions

Question 1: What does Hank like to do?

[ ] a. Have parties

[ ] b. Go swimming

[ ] c. Take naps

[ ] d. Watch TV

Question 2: What happens when Hank gets excited?

[ ] a. He sneezes confetti

[ ] b. He gets a headache

[ ] c. He dances

[ ] d. He falls asleep

Question 3: How did Hank's friends feel about his confetti sneezing at first?

[ ] a. Annoyed

[ ] b. Excited

[ ] c. Indifferent

[ ] d. Surprised

Question 4: What solution did Hank come up with to make everyone happy?

[ ] a. To stop throwing parties

[ ] b. To move away

[ ] c. To have a confetti party

[ ] d. To keep sneezing confetti

Story 7: Animal Parade

Once upon a time, in a magical forest, all of the animals decided to have a parade. The parade was going to be led by the wisest animal in the forest, the owl. The owl was very excited to lead the parade, and all of the animals were excited to follow.

On the day of the parade, all of the animals gathered at the starting point. The owl, perched on a tree branch, gave a hoot, and the parade began. The rabbit hopped, the deer pranced, and the bear lumbered along. All of the animals were having a great time, but they wanted to make the parade even more special.

The animals decided to sing a song together. They had a little trouble at first, as they all had different voices, but with some practice, they managed to harmonize. The song echoed through the forest, and all of the animals joined in. It was a beautiful moment.

As they reached the end of the parade, they all felt happy and proud. They had worked together to make something special, and they had all had fun. The owl gave a final hoot, and the animals dispersed, looking forward to the next parade.

> **★ Definition**
> Harmonize—to bring different things into agreement, consistency, or harmony, often in terms of music, ideas, or actions.

Reading Comprehension Questions

Question 1: Who led the animal parade?

[ ] a. The rabbit

[ ] b. The deer

[ ] c. The bear

[ ] d. The owl

Question 2: What did the animals decide to do to make the parade more special?

[ ] a. Sing a song

[ ] b. Run faster

[ ] c. Hide

[ ] d. Eat snacks

Question 3: What did the animals do at the end of the parade?

[ ] a. Argue with each other

[ ] b. Hug each other

[ ] c. Disperse

[ ] d. Start another parade

Question 4: How did the animals feel at the end of the parade?

[ ] a. Sad and disappointed

[ ] b. Angry and frustrated

[ ] c. Happy and proud

[ ] d. Confused and worried

Story 8: Alien Food Fight

The aliens were having a great time at their space picnic when they suddenly started throwing food at each other. The purple alien threw a piece of space fruit at the green alien, who retaliated by tossing a space sandwich. Soon, all the aliens were involved in the food fight, laughing and shouting as they hurled space snacks at each other.

The blue alien, who was watching from a distance, felt sad because she didn't like to waste food. She decided to try to stop the food fight by talking to the other aliens. The blue alien asked them if they knew how much energy it took to produce the food they were throwing.

The other aliens didn't know, so the blue alien explained that it was important to respect food and not waste it.

The other aliens felt bad about wasting food and decided to stop the food fight. They all gathered around and shared their space snacks, making sure not to waste any more food.

Reading Comprehension Questions

Question 1: What were the aliens doing before they started the food fight?

_____

_____

_____

Question 2: Why did the blue alien feel sad during the food fight?

_____

_____

_____

Question 3: What did the blue alien do to stop the food fight?

_____

_____

_____

Question 4: How did the aliens resolve the food fight?

_____

_____

_____

Story 9: The Secret Life of Toys

RL.2.1
RL.2.3
RL.2.7
RL.2.9

Have you ever wondered what toys do when we're not playing with them? Well, in a world where toys can come to life, they have quite the adventure! Toys of all kinds, from teddy bears to robots, gather together and come to life when their owners leave the room. They talk, they play, and sometimes they even go on wild adventures. But when their owners come back, they quickly freeze and pretend to be just regular toys again.

One day, a new toy arrived in the playroom. His name was Neon Blaze, and he was a superhero! He was excited to join in on the fun and games, but the other toys were hesitant to accept him at first. They had never seen anything like him before. But soon, they realized that Neon was a great addition to their group, and they all became friends.

As the night went on, the toys had a dance party, played games, and even snuck into the kitchen to get some snacks. But they always made sure to freeze when their owners came back. It was a fun and exciting night, and they couldn't wait to do it all again tomorrow!

For Fun! Draw your favorite toy!

Reading Comprehension Questions

Question 1: What do the toys do when their owners leave the room?

_____

_____

_____

Question 2: How do the other toys react when Neon Blaze arrives?

_____

_____

_____

Question 3: What do the toys do when they sneak into the kitchen?

_____

_____

_____

Question 4: Why do the toys freeze when their owners come back?

_____

_____

_____

Story 10: Samantha's Silly Word Problem

Samantha loved to play with words. She loved the way they sounded and how they could make people laugh. One day, she discovered a word that made her giggle so much that she couldn't stop saying it. The word was "flibbertigibbet." Samantha would say it over and over again until her friends got tired of hearing it. But she couldn't stop. The next day, she discovered another silly word, "ballyhoo." She said it so much that it got stuck in her head. She even said it during class and got in trouble. Samantha realized she needed to find a way to control her love for silly words.

For Fun! Create your own list of silly words!

1. _____

2. _____

3. _____

4. _____

5. _____

Reading Comprehension Questions

Question 1: What did Samantha love to do with words?

_____

_____

_____

Question 2: What is the silly word Samantha discovered that made her giggle?

_____

_____

_____

Question 3: What happened when Samantha said silly words during class?

_____

_____

_____

Question 4: Why did Samantha realize she needed to control her love for silly words?

_____

_____

_____

Story 11: The Wizard's Special Day

There was once a wizard who had been working on a new spell for months, and he was eager to try it out. He decided to visit the amusement park, where he could have some fun while testing his magic.

As he entered the park, he used his wand to make himself invisible. He wandered around the park, watching people scream on roller coasters and laugh on carousels. He even made a cotton candy stand's delicious treat turn purple with a flick of his wand!

Suddenly, he heard a child crying. He saw a little girl who had lost her favorite teddy bear on a ride. The wizard knew just what to do. He pointed his wand at the ride and muttered the spell. Suddenly, the teddy bear appeared next to the little girl, and she hugged it tightly.

Feeling proud of himself, the wizard decided to try one more spell. He pointed his wand at a game booth where a little boy was struggling and whispered the magic words. Suddenly, the balls began to fly into the baskets, one after the other. The carnival worker looked shocked and gave the boy a huge stuffed animal.

As the day ended, the wizard realized that he had experienced more fun than he had in a long time. He decided that he would come back to the amusement park, but next time he would leave his wand at home.

Reading Comprehension Questions

Question 1: Why did the wizard go to the amusement park?

_____

_____

_____

Question 2: What did the wizard do to make himself invisible?

_____

_____

_____

Question 3: How did the wizard help the little girl who had lost her teddy bear?

_____

_____

_____

Question 4: How will the wizard's next visit to the amusement park be different from the first time?

_____

_____

Story 12: The Silliest Story in the World

Once upon a time, there was a silly storyteller named Sam. He loved to tell silly stories to anyone who would listen. One day, he decided to tell the silliest story in the world.

Once there was a cow that could talk. She would tell jokes to all the other animals on the farm. One day, she told a joke that was so funny, all the animals laughed so hard that they started to float in the air. The farmer saw this and was so surprised that he fainted!

The cow saw that the farmer had fainted and knew that she had to do something. So, she flew over to the farmer and started to tickle him. The farmer woke up and saw all the animals floating in the air. He couldn't believe his eyes!

Suddenly, a group of aliens landed their spaceship on the farm. They saw all the animals floating and thought that the farm was a new kind of amusement park. They got out of their spaceship and started to ride the animals like they were carnival rides!

The cow and all the other animals were having so much fun that they didn't want the aliens to leave. So, they convinced the aliens to stay on the farm forever and ride them like carnival rides every day.

And that, my friends, is the silliest story in the world.

Reading Comprehension Questions

Question 1: What did the cow do to make the farmer wake up?

_____

_____

_____

Question 2: Why did the aliens land their spaceship on the farm?

_____

_____

_____

Question 3: What did the animals convince the aliens to do?

_____

_____

_____

Question 4: What was the storyteller's name?

_____

_____

_____

Story 13: Magnolia the Explorer

Magnolia was a second grader who loved exploring the world around her. She had a bright smile that could light up any room she entered. The only difference between Magnolia and her classmates was that she used a wheelchair to get around. Even though her wheelchair made things a little harder for her, Magnolia never let it hold her back.

One day, Magnolia's class was going on a field trip to the zoo. She was so excited to see all the animals and learn new things. However, when they arrived at the zoo, Magnolia realized that some of the exhibits were not accessible to her wheelchair.

Magnolia was disappointed, but she didn't let that stop her. She decided to make the best of the situation and explore the parts of the zoo that she could access. She even found a few hidden paths that her classmates didn't know about!

As they were leaving the zoo, Magnolia's teacher asked the class what their favorite part of the trip was. Magnolia raised her hand and said, "My favorite part was finding new paths that I never knew existed!" Everyone was amazed and inspired by Magnolia's positive attitude.

From that day on, Magnolia became known as the explorer in her class. She taught her classmates to never give up and to always find a way to make the best of any situation.

Reading Comprehension Questions

Question 1: What was the difference between Magnolia and her classmates?

[ ] a. Magnolia had blonde hair

[ ] b. Magnolia used a wheelchair

[ ] c. Magnolia was taller than her classmates

[ ] d. Magnolia had a pet cat

Question 2: Where did Magnolia's class go on a field trip?

[ ] a. The aquarium

[ ] b. The museum

[ ] c. The zoo

[ ] d. The park

Question 3: What did Magnolia do when she realized some of the exhibits were not accessible to her wheelchair?

[ ] a. She gave up and went back to the bus

[ ] b. She complained to her teacher

[ ] c. She explored the parts of the zoo she could access

[ ] d. She stayed in one spot and watched the other kids

Question 4: What did Magnolia teach her classmates?

[ ] a. To never give up

[ ] b. To always complain to the teacher

[ ] c. To stay in one spot and watch the other kids

[ ] d. To be mean to people who are different

Story 14: Penelope's Big Surprise

Penelope was a second-grade student who loved robots. She had always been fascinated by how they worked and how they could make our lives easier. So, when her teacher announced that they would be doing a class project on robots, Penelope was thrilled.

Penelope worked hard on her project and even built a robot from scratch. She programmed it to do simple tasks like pick up pencils and move around. However, when she presented her project to the class, something strange happened. The robot started moving on its own!

The class was amazed, and Penelope was in shock. She had no idea how her robot had come to life. However, she soon realized that she had accidentally programmed the robot to have an AI (Artificial Intelligence) system. This meant that the robot could learn and improve on its own.

Penelope's teacher was so impressed that she suggested that Penelope enter her robot into a science fair. Penelope was hesitant at first, but she soon realized that this was an opportunity of a lifetime.

She spent the next few weeks improving her robot and adding new features. When the day of the science fair arrived, Penelope was nervous but excited. Her robot was the star of the show and everyone wanted to see it in action.

The judges were impressed with Penelope's project and awarded her first place. Penelope was overjoyed, and her robot had become famous overnight. From that day on, Penelope became known as the girl who built a robot that came to life.

Reading Comprehension Questions

Question 1: What was Penelope's class project about?

[ ] a. Dinosaurs

[ ] b. Robots

[ ] c. Plants

[ ] d. Cars

Question 2: What happened when Penelope presented her project to the class?

[ ] a. The robot started moving on its own

[ ] b. The robot broke

[ ] c. The class laughed at her

[ ] d. The teacher was not impressed

Question 3: Why was Penelope hesitant to enter her robot into a science fair?

[ ] a. She was afraid of losing

[ ] b. She didn't think her robot was good enough

[ ] c. She didn't want her robot to become famous

[ ] d. She was too busy with other things

Question 4: What did Penelope become known as after the science fair?

[ ] a. The girl who built a time machine

[ ] b. The girl who built a robot that could fly

[ ] c. The girl who built a robot that came to life

[ ] d. The girl who built a rocket ship to Mars

For Fun! Draw your own robot that comes to life!

Story 15: Howling for Speed

Ciena had always loved cars. She loved the way they moved and the sound of their engines revving. So, it was no surprise to anyone when she announced that she wanted to become a race car driver. Her parents were hesitant at first, but they could see the passion in her eyes and they decided to support her dream.

Ciena started racing at a young age, and she quickly became one of the best racers in her town. But what made her even more unique was that she raced with her two huskies, Skylie and Bear. They would sit in the back seat and howl with excitement as they sped around the track.

Ciena loved racing with her dogs. She would often talk to them during the race, telling them to hold on tight as they went around the curves. Her competitors thought it was strange at first, but they soon realized that it was just part of Ciena's charm.

One day, Ciena and her dogs were invited to compete in a big race in the city. It was a tough competition, with many skilled racers from all over the state. But Ciena was determined to win.

As the race began, Ciena and her dogs took off, their car moving faster than ever before. They went around the curves with precision and zoomed down the straightaways with ease. The crowd was amazed as they watched the young girl and her huskies take the lead.

In the end, Ciena and her dogs won the race, much to the delight of the cheering crowd. It was a moment that Ciena would never forget, and it proved to her that anything is possible when you have the courage to follow your dreams.

Reading Comprehension Questions

Question 1: What does Ciena want to be when she grows up?

[ ] a. A teacher

[ ] b. A race car driver

[ ] c. A doctor

[ ] d. A chef

Question 2: Who does Ciena race with?

[ ] a. Her friends

[ ] b. Her siblings

[ ] c. Her parents

[ ] d. Her huskies, Skylie and Bear

Question 3: What do Ciena's competitors think of her racing with her dogs?

[ ] a. They think it's funny

[ ] b. They think it's strange

[ ] c. They think it's cool

[ ] d. They don't notice

Question 4: What happens at the end of the race?

[ ] a. Ciena and her dogs lose

[ ] b. Ciena and her dogs crash

[ ] c. Ciena and her dogs win

[ ] d. Ciena and her dogs quit

Section 2

INFORMATIONAL TEXTS

Informational text is a type of text that provides factual information about a topic, event, or concept. It is designed to inform and educate readers, rather than entertain them like narrative or fictional texts. Examples of informational texts include newspapers, textbooks, biographies, and encyclopedias.

In second grade, it is important for students to learn how to comprehend and analyze informational texts because it helps them build knowledge and vocabulary, expand their understanding of the world around them, and develop critical thinking and problem-solving skills.

Reading Skills

Before you jump into the full stories in this section, brush up on your reading skills with the activities on the following pages.

 Preview the Text

 Stop and Ask Questions

 Identify Key Details

 Use Text Features

Come back to this page and color in the stars after you finish each activity!

Reading Skill: Preview the Text

Read the following title and subheading:

The Incredible Rainforest
Diverse Ecosystems

Answer the following questions:

Take a look at the title for this text. What do you think the story might be about?

_____

_____

Based on the subheading, what can you infer about the rainforest?

_____

_____

Share one thing you already know or have heard about the rainforest.

_____

_____

Read the text:

> The rainforest is a remarkable place filled with countless plants and animals. It is known for its dense vegetation, tall trees, and abundant rainfall. In this passage, we will explore the various ecosystems found within the rainforest and learn about the amazing creatures that call it home.

Reading Skill: Stop and Ask Questions

Read the following text:

Amazing Dolphins

Dolphins are fascinating marine mammals that live in oceans all around the world. They are known for their intelligence, playful nature, and acrobatic skills. Dolphins belong to the cetacean family, which also includes whales and porpoises.

Pause and think about what you just read. Write one question you have about the text:

_____

These incredible creatures have streamlined bodies that help them swim gracefully through the water. They have a blowhole on the top of their heads, which allows them to breathe air at the water's surface. Dolphins use their powerful tails, called flukes, to propel themselves through the water at impressive speeds.

Pause and think about what you just read. Write one question you have about the text:

_____

One of the most amazing things about dolphins is their communication skills. They use a series of clicks, whistles, and body movements to communicate with each other. Scientists believe that dolphins have their own unique language, and they use it to work together when hunting for food or protecting their pod.

Pause and think about what you just read. Write one question you have about the text:

_____

Dolphins are social animals and usually live in groups called pods. These pods can vary in size from just a few dolphins to several hundred. Within a pod, dolphins take care of each other and work together to find food and navigate the ocean.

Pause and think about what you just read. What answers to your questions did you learn as you continued reading?

_____

Reading Skill: Identify Key Details

Read the following text:

The History of Clowns

Clowns have a long history. They started in ancient times and were known for their funny acts and silly outfits. During the Middle Ages, jesters entertained the rich with tricks and jokes. Clowns became popular in circuses in the 18th and 19th centuries. Today, clowns still make people laugh at circuses and parties.

Identify the following important ideas:

Where did clowns become popular performers?

_____

Name one way clowns entertained people during the Middle Ages.

_____

Where can you find clowns today?

_____

☆ Reading Skill: Use Text Features

Read the following text:

Exploring the Mail System

The mail system is a way to send and receive letters and packages. It involves several steps and different people who help ensure that your mail reaches its destination.

Parts of the Mail System
Mailboxes and Post Office

Mailboxes are where you drop off your outgoing mail. They are usually found on the streets or near your home. The mail carrier, a person who delivers the mail, collects the letters and packages from the mailboxes and takes them to the post office. The post office is like a central hub for all the mail. Here, the mail is sorted, organized, and prepared for delivery.

Picture of a Mail Carrier

Steps in the Mail System
Sorting and Delivery

Once the mail reaches the post office, it goes through a sorting process. Mail is separated based on its destination, such as different cities or states. Then, the mail carriers take the sorted mail and deliver it to the correct addresses. They use trucks, bikes, or even walk to deliver the mail to homes and businesses.

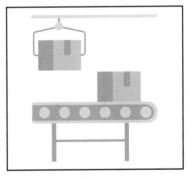

Picture of Mail Sorting

Look at the picture of the mail carrier. What is the role of a mail carrier in the mail system?

Explain the purpose of mailboxes in the mail system.

Information 1: The History of Television

RI.2.1
RI.2.3

Television has been around for over 100 years. It started out as a way for people to see moving pictures, but it quickly evolved into a way to watch news, sports, and entertainment. The first television sets were very different from the ones we have today. They were black and white, and the screens were small. But people were still amazed by them.

In the 1950s, television became very popular. More and more people were buying sets and watching shows every day. The shows were often silly and fun, but they could also be educational. People were learning new things from the comfort of their own homes. Today, television is still an important part of our lives, and it has evolved even further. We now have color TVs, flat screens, and even streaming services that let us watch our favorite shows whenever we want.

Reading Comprehension Questions

Question 1: What was the original purpose of television?

_____

_____

_____

Question 2: What was different about the first television sets compared to the ones we have today?

_____

_____

_____

Question 3: What were some types of shows people watched on television in the 1950s?

_____

_____

_____

Question 4: What are some advancements in television technology today?

_____

_____

_____

Information 2: Space Exploration

Space exploration is the study and exploration of outer space. Humans have been interested in space for thousands of years, but it wasn't until the 20th century that we had the technology to explore it. Today, we have sent spacecraft to study planets, asteroids, and comets, and we have even sent humans to walk on the moon. Space exploration has helped us learn more about our universe and the world we live in.

One reason space exploration is important is that it helps us learn more about our own planet. By studying other planets and moons, we can learn about the forces that shaped our own planet. We can also learn more about how our own planet works. For example, scientists have studied Mars to learn more about the history of water on our planet.

Another reason space exploration is important is that it helps us understand the universe. By studying stars, galaxies, and other celestial bodies, we can learn more about how the universe works. We can also learn more about the origins of the universe and how it will evolve in the future.

Despite the benefits of space exploration, there are also challenges. Spacecraft must travel long distances, often taking years to reach their destinations. They must also be designed to survive extreme conditions, such as the vacuum of space and extreme temperatures. Additionally, space exploration is expensive, and it requires significant investment from governments and private companies.

Reading Comprehension Questions

Question 1: Why is space exploration important?

[ ] a. To learn more about our own planet

[ ] b. To study other countries

[ ] c. To build more spacecraft

[ ] d. To create new technology

Question 2: What have humans done in space exploration?

[ ] a. Sent spacecraft to study other planets

[ ] b. Sent humans to walk on the moon

[ ] c. Studied stars, galaxies, and other celestial bodies

[ ] d. All of the above

Question 3: What are some challenges of space exploration?

[ ] a. Traveling long distances and surviving extreme conditions

[ ] b. Designing spacecraft to be small and lightweight

[ ] c. Finding funding for space exploration

[ ] d. All of the above

Question 4: What have scientists learned about our planet from studying Mars?

[ ] a. How to build spacecraft

[ ] b. How to create new technology

[ ] c. The history of water on Earth

[ ] d. The origins of the universe

Information 3: What Makes Airplanes Fly?

Airplanes are fascinating machines that can soar through the air at high speeds. But how do they do it? The key to flight is the way airplanes use their wings to create lift. The shape of an airplane's wings is curved on the top and flat on the bottom. When the airplane moves forward, air flows over the curved top of the wings and under the flat bottom of the wings. This causes the air pressure on top of the wings to be lower than the air pressure on the bottom of the wings, which creates an upward force called lift. This lift allows the airplane to stay in the air and even climb higher.

In addition to lift, airplanes use thrust to move forward. Thrust is created by the airplane's engines, which push the airplane through the air. Once the airplane is moving, it can control its direction and altitude using its tail and flaps.

Reading Comprehension Questions

Question 1: What is the key to flight for airplanes?

_____

_____

Question 2: What is the shape of an airplane's wings?

_____

_____

Question 3: How does an airplane create thrust?

_____

_____

Question 4: What parts of an airplane allow it to control its direction and altitude?

_____

_____

Information 4: How Human Brains Work

RI.2.2
RI.2.3
RI.2.4

The human brain is an amazing organ that controls everything we do, from breathing and moving to thinking and feeling. The brain is made up of billions of cells called neurons, which communicate with each other through electrical and chemical signals. These signals help us to process information and make decisions.

Different parts of the brain are responsible for different functions. For example, the frontal lobe is responsible for decision making and problem solving, while the occipital lobe is responsible for processing visual information. The brain also has a part called the hippocampus that helps us to form and store memories.

When we learn new things or practice a skill, our brain forms new connections between neurons. These connections allow us to improve our abilities and make tasks easier over time. However, the brain also needs rest and sleep in order to function properly.

Reading Comprehension Questions

Question 1: What are the cells in the brain called?

_____

_____

Question 2: How do neurons communicate with each other?

_____

_____

Question 3: What is the occipital lobe responsible for?

_____

_____

Question 4: Why is rest and sleep important for the brain?

_____

_____

Information 5: All About Carpentry

Carpentry is the art and science of working with wood to create beautiful and functional objects. Carpenters use a variety of tools, such as hammers, saws, chisels, and drills, to cut, shape, and join pieces of wood.

One of the most important skills in carpentry is measuring accurately. Carpenters use rulers, tape measures, and squares to measure the length, width, and thickness of the wood they are working with. They also use these tools to mark where they need to make cuts or drill holes.

Another important skill in carpentry is the ability to join pieces of wood together. Carpenters use a variety of techniques to join wood, including nails, screws, glue, and dovetail joints. They also use clamps to hold pieces of wood together while they work.

Carpentry can be used to create a wide range of objects, from furniture and cabinets to houses and bridges. It is a skill that requires patience, precision, and creativity.

Reading Comprehension Questions

Question 1: What is carpentry?

_____

_____

_____

Question 2: What tools do carpenters use?

_____

_____

_____

Question 3: Why is measuring accurately important in carpentry?

_____

_____

_____

Question 4: What is one way carpenters join pieces of wood together?

_____

_____

_____

RI.2.1
RI.2.3
RI.2.7
RI.2.8

The first zoo was established in Egypt over 4,500 years ago. It was called the "House of Anubis," and it was located in a temple in the city of Hierakonpolis. The zoo housed many different animals, including elephants, lions, baboons, and even a hippopotamus. The animals were kept in large enclosures made of mud and brick, and they were fed and cared for by priests.

The House of Anubis was not just a place to display animals. It was also a religious center where people came to worship the gods. The priests who cared for the animals believed that they were sacred and had special powers. They also believed that by caring for the animals, they were serving the gods.

Over time, zoos became more common throughout the world. Today, there are thousands of zoos that house millions of animals. While some people argue that zoos are necessary for conservation and education, others believe that they are cruel and unnecessary. Regardless of one's opinion, the first zoo in Egypt played an important role in the history of human-animal relationships.

Reading Comprehension Questions

Question 1: Where was the first zoo located?

_____

_____

Question 2: What types of animals were housed in the first zoo?

_____

_____

Question 3: What was the purpose of the House of Anubis besides being a place for displaying animals?

_____

_____

Question 4: What are some differing opinions about zoos today?

_____

_____

Information 7: How Crayons Are Made

Crayons are a popular art supply for kids of all ages. Have you ever wondered how crayons are made? It's actually a pretty interesting process!

The first step in making crayons is to melt wax. The wax is usually a mixture of different types of paraffin wax and color pigment. The wax is heated to a temperature of about 200 degrees Fahrenheit until it is completely melted.

Once the wax is melted, it is poured into a mold that is shaped like a crayon. The mold is cooled until the wax solidifies and takes on the shape of the mold.

After the crayons are cooled and solidified, they are removed from the mold and labeled with their color name. The crayons are then sorted into boxes and packaged for sale.

Did you know that crayons were invented in the early 1900s by a company called Binney & Smith? They created the Crayola brand of crayons, which is still one of the most popular brands today!

Reading Comprehension Questions

Question 1: What is the first step in making crayons?

[ ] a. Labeling the crayons with their color name

[ ] b. Heating the wax to a high temperature

[ ] c. Pouring the wax into a mold

[ ] d. Sorting the crayons into boxes

Question 2: What is the wax usually made of?

[ ] a. Water and color pigment

[ ] b. Flour and sugar

[ ] c. Paraffin wax and color pigment

[ ] d. Oil and vinegar

Question 3: How are the crayons shaped?

[ ] a. They are cut into shape with a machine

[ ] b. They are hand-carved by artists

[ ] c. They are poured into a mold

[ ] d. They are shaped by a 3D printer

Question 4: Who invented crayons?

[ ] a. Binney & Smith

[ ] b. Thomas Edison

[ ] c. Alexander Graham Bell

[ ] d. Albert Einstein

Information 8: The Perfect Pancake Recipe

Making pancakes is a fun and easy activity that many people enjoy doing. Pancakes are a breakfast food that is usually served with butter and syrup. Here is a simple recipe to make pancakes:

Ingredients:
1 cup flour
2 teaspoons baking powder
1/2 teaspoon salt
2 tablespoons sugar
1 egg
1 cup milk
2 tablespoons vegetable oil

Instructions:
1. In a mixing bowl, combine the flour, baking powder, salt, and sugar.
2. In a separate bowl, beat the egg and then add the milk and vegetable oil.
3. Add the wet ingredients to the dry ingredients and mix until the batter is smooth.
4. Heat a nonstick pan or griddle over medium heat.
5. Scoop 1/4 cup of batter onto the pan for each pancake.
6. Cook the pancake until bubbles form on the surface and the edges start to look dry, then flip it over and cook for another 1-2 minutes on the other side.
7. Repeat with the remaining batter until all the pancakes are cooked.

Reading Comprehension Questions

Question 1: What are pancakes usually served with?

[ ] a. Ketchup

[ ] b. Butter and syrup

[ ] c. Salad

[ ] d. Orange juice

Question 2: What do you need to do before adding wet ingredients to dry ingredients?

[ ] a. Put them in separate bowls

[ ] a. Mix them together

[ ] b. Add salt

[ ] c. Let them sit for an hour

Question 3: How do you know when to flip the pancake over?

[ ] a. When it's burned

[ ] b. When it's still raw

[ ] c. When bubbles form on the surface and the edges start to look dry

[ ] d. When it's completely flat

Question 4: What is the purpose of step 4 in the recipe?

[ ] a. To cool down the pan

[ ] b. To test the pancake batter

[ ] c. To make sure the batter is hot enough

[ ] d. To prepare the pan for cooking the pancakes

Information 9: Weird Weather

Weather can be strange and unpredictable. Sometimes, it can even be downright weird! Here are some examples of weird weather:

1. Red rain: In some parts of the world, rain can be red. This can happen when dust or sand from the desert is blown up into the atmosphere and mixes with rain clouds.

2. Snow rollers: Snow rollers are a rare weather phenomenon that occurs when snowballs are formed naturally by the wind. They are shaped like giant jelly rolls and are hollow in the center.

3. Sun dogs: Sun dogs are bright spots that appear on either side of the sun. They are caused by the reflection and refraction of sunlight by ice crystals in the atmosphere.

4. Fire tornadoes: Fire tornadoes, also known as fire whirls, are whirlwinds that are created when intense heat and turbulent winds combine. They can be dangerous and destructive.

These are just a few examples of weird weather that can happen around the world. While they may seem strange, they are all just part of the natural world around us.

Reading Comprehension Questions

Question 1: What is red rain?

[　] a.　Rain that is green in color

[　] b.　Rain that is red in color

[　] c.　Rain that is blue in color

[　] d.　Rain that is yellow in color

Question 2: What are snow rollers?

[　] a.　A type of candy

[　] b.　A rare weather phenomenon where snowballs are formed naturally by the wind

[　] c.　A type of sled

[　] d.　A type of snowflake

Question 3: What causes sun dogs?

[　] a.　The reflection and refraction of sunlight by ice crystals in the atmosphere

[　] b.　The reflection and refraction of sunlight by water droplets in the atmosphere

[　] c.　The reflection and refraction of moonlight by ice crystals in the atmosphere

[　] d.　The reflection and refraction of moonlight by water droplets in the atmosphere

Question 4: What are fire tornadoes?

[　] a.　Whirlwinds created by intense heat and turbulent winds

[　] b.　Whirlwinds created by rain and wind

[　] c.　Whirlwinds created by snow and wind

[　] d.　Whirlwinds created by dust and wind

Plants have a life cycle, just like animals do. The life cycle of a plant begins with a seed. Inside the seed is a tiny plant called an embryo. The seed needs water, air, and warmth to germinate, which means to start growing.

Once the seed has germinated, a small root grows down into the soil, and a stem with leaves grows up toward the sun. This stage is called the seedling stage.

As the plant grows, it begins to develop flowers. The flowers attract bees and other insects that help pollinate them. Pollination is when pollen from the male part of the flower (the stamen) fertilizes the female part of the flower (the pistil).

After the flower is pollinated, the plant produces fruit that contains seeds. The fruit is eaten by animals, and the seeds are dispersed (spread around) through their waste.

Eventually, the plant dies, and the cycle starts again with the seeds that were dispersed. This is how plants continue to grow and reproduce.

Reading Comprehension Questions

Question 1: What is the first stage in the life cycle of a plant?

[ ] a. Germination

[ ] b. Pollination

[ ] c. Fruit production

[ ] d. Seed dispersal

Question 2: What is pollination?

[ ] a. When pollen from the male part of the flower fertilizes the female part of the flower

[ ] b. When seeds are dispersed by the wind

[ ] c. When a seed begins to grow

[ ] d. When a plant produces fruit

Question 3: How are seeds dispersed?

[ ] a. By bees and other insects

[ ] b. By the wind

[ ] c. Through animal waste

[ ] d. By birds

Question 4: What happens to the plant after it produces fruit?

[ ] a. It dies

[ ] b. It continues to grow without producing more seeds

[ ] c. It starts the pollination process again

[ ] d. It enters the seedling stage

Information 11: Magnets Are Amazing!

Magnets are amazing objects that have the power to attract certain types of metal. They work by creating a magnetic field, which is a force that pulls on other magnetic materials.

Inside a magnet, there are small particles called electrons. These electrons spin in the same direction, which creates a magnetic field around the magnet. This field is strongest at the ends of the magnet, which are called the North and South poles.

When two magnets are brought near each other, the opposite poles (North and South) attract each other, while the like poles (North and North or South and South) repel each other. This is because the magnetic field lines from each magnet are either attracted to or repelled by the field lines from the other magnet.

Magnets are used in many different ways, from holding notes on a refrigerator to powering machines in factories. They are also used in compasses, which help people find their way by pointing towards the North Pole.

Reading Comprehension Questions

Question 1: How do magnets work?

_____

_____

_____

Question 2: What is the strongest part of a magnet?

_____

_____

_____

Question 3: What happens when opposite poles of two magnets are brought near each other?

_____

_____

_____

Question 4: Name one way magnets are used.

_____

_____

_____

Information 12: All About Volcanoes

Volcanoes are amazing and powerful geological features found on Earth. A volcano is essentially a mountain with a vent or opening in the Earth's crust, through which molten rock, ash, and gasses can escape. There are many different types of volcanoes, each with its own characteristics and eruption style.

When a volcano erupts, it can cause destruction in the surrounding areas. Lava flows can destroy homes and buildings, and ash can cause problems for transportation and agriculture. However, volcanoes also have benefits. The ash and rock that are ejected during an eruption can enrich the soil, and hot springs and geysers formed by volcanic activity can provide sources of energy.

For Fun! Go through the maze to escape the volcano!

Reading Comprehension Questions

Question 1: What is a volcano?

[ ] a. A type of tree

[ ] b. A mountain with an opening in the Earth's crust

[ ] c. A body of water

Question 2: What can lava flows do?

[ ] a. Create new homes

[ ] b. Help farmers grow crops

[ ] c. Destroy homes and buildings

Question 3: What benefits do volcanoes have?

[ ] a. They create new mountains

[ ] b. They enrich the soil and provide sources of energy

[ ] c. They cause destruction in the surrounding areas

Question 4: What are some things that can be ejected during a volcano eruption?

[ ] a. Rocks and ash

[ ] b. Flowers and bees

[ ] c. Fish and seaweed

Information 13: The History of Theater

RI.2.1
RI.2.3

Reading Comprehension Questions

Question 1: Where did people in ancient Greece gather to watch plays and performances?

_____

_____

_____

Question 2: What were some of the stories often told in ancient Greek plays?

_____

_____

_____

Question 3: Who became one of the most famous playwrights in history in the 16th century?

_____

_____

_____

Question 4: Where can people watch plays and musicals today?

_____

_____

_____

Theater has been an important part of human culture for thousands of years. In ancient Greece, people would gather in outdoor amphitheaters to watch plays and performances. These plays often told stories about gods and goddesses, and were performed by actors wearing masks to represent different characters.

During the Middle Ages in Europe, theater was often performed by traveling groups of actors who would travel from town to town to put on shows. These performances were often based on stories from the Bible or other religious texts.

In the 16th century, William Shakespeare became one of the most famous playwrights in history. He wrote many plays that are still performed today, including Romeo and Juliet and Hamlet. During Shakespeare's time, theater was often performed in indoor theaters, which allowed for more elaborate sets and costumes.

Today, theater is still an important form of entertainment around the world. People can watch plays and musicals in theaters, as well as on television and online.

Information 14: All About Skyscrapers

RI.2.1
RI.2.3

Skyscrapers are tall buildings that can be found in many cities around the world. These buildings are called "skyscrapers" because they are so tall, they seem to scrape the sky.

Skyscrapers are built with strong materials such as steel and concrete. They are designed to be able to withstand high winds and earthquakes. In the past, buildings could only be a few stories tall because they were made of weaker materials like wood and brick.

The first skyscraper was built in Chicago in 1885. It was called the Home Insurance Building and was 10 stories tall. The building was made of steel and had an elevator to take people to the top floors.

Today, skyscrapers can be found all over the world, with the tallest one being the Burj Khalifa in Dubai, which is over 828 meters (2,716 feet) tall. Skyscrapers are used for many things, including offices, hotels, apartments, and restaurants.

Reading Comprehension Questions

Question 1: What are skyscrapers?

_____

_____

Question 2: What are skyscrapers made of?

_____

_____

Question 3: What was the first skyscraper ever built and where was it built?

_____

_____

Question 4: What is the tallest skyscraper in the world?

_____

_____

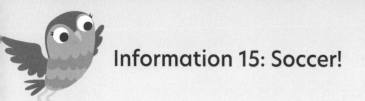

Information 15: Soccer!

RI.2.1
RI.2.2
RI.2.3

Soccer, also known as football in many countries, is a popular sport played all over the world. It is a game that involves two teams of eleven players each who try to score points by kicking a ball into the opposing team's goal.

The history of soccer can be traced back to ancient times when people played similar games in various parts of the world. However, the modern game of soccer as we know it today originated in England in the 19th century.

To play soccer, players need to wear special shoes called cleats that have spikes on the bottom to help them grip the ground. They also wear shorts, shirts, and socks in their team colors.

During a soccer game, players try to pass the ball to their teammates using their feet, and they try to take the ball away from the opposing team by kicking it or intercepting it. The goalie, who wears a different colored shirt, tries to block the ball from entering their team's goal.

Soccer is a popular sport because it is easy to learn and can be played by people of all ages and skill levels. It is also a great way to stay active and healthy.

Reading Comprehension Questions

Question 1: What is soccer?

[ ] a. A sport played underwater

[ ] b. A sport played with a ball and two teams of eleven players each

[ ] c. A game played with sticks and a ball

Question 2: Where did the modern game of soccer originate?

[ ] a. Japan

[ ] b. Brazil

[ ] c. England

Question 3: What do soccer players wear on their feet to help them grip the ground?

[ ] a. Sneakers

[ ] b. Cleats

[ ] c. Sandals

Question 4: Why is soccer a popular sport?

[ ] a. It is easy to learn and can be played by people of all ages and skill levels

[ ] b. It is a dangerous sport that requires a lot of physical strength

[ ] c. It can only be played by professional athletes

Section 3

BIOGRAPHICAL TEXTS

Biographical text is a type of informational text that tells the story of a person's life. It typically includes information about the person's background, achievements, challenges, and contributions to society. Biographies can be written about historical figures, famous individuals, or ordinary people who have made a significant impact on the world.

In second grade, it is important for students to learn how to comprehend and analyze biographical texts because it helps them develop their understanding of history and the world around them. Biographies allow students to learn about the lives of important people who have made a difference, and how their actions and contributions have influenced society.

Biographical texts help students develop empathy and a sense of understanding towards people from different backgrounds and cultures. The ability to read and comprehend biographical texts is an important skill for second graders to develop as they build their knowledge and understanding of the world.

Reading Skills

Before you jump into the full stories in this section, brush up on your reading skills with the activities on the following pages.

 Identify the Main Idea   Use Context Clues

 Determine the
Author's Purpose   Compare and Contrast

Come back to this page
and color in the stars after
you finish each activity!

Reading Skill: Identify the Main Idea

Read the following text:

Jane Goodall: *A Life Dedicated to Chimpanzees*

Jane Goodall is a scientist who studied and protected chimpanzees. She observed their behavior and learned that they are intelligent and have complex social lives. Jane's work helped us understand animals better and inspired conservation efforts.

Who is this passage about?

_____

What did Jane Goodall study and protect?

_____

 # Reading Skill: Determine the Author's Purpose

Read the following text:

Ruby Bridges: *A Brave Trailblazer*

Ruby Bridges was a courageous young girl who made history by being the first African American student to attend an all-white school. In 1960, at the age of six, Ruby walked through the doors of William Frantz Elementary School in New Orleans, Louisiana, surrounded by angry protesters. Despite facing discrimination and hatred, Ruby showed great strength and determination.

Who is Ruby Bridges?

_____

Why did the author write this biography?

_____

Food for Thought

The author wrote this biography to inform readers about Ruby Bridges and her significant role in the civil rights movement. By sharing Ruby's story, the author wants to inspire others to stand up for equality and fight against injustice!

Reading Skill: Use Context Clues

Read the following text:

Sitting Bull: *A Fearless Leader*

Sitting Bull was a famous Native American chief of the Lakota Sioux tribe. He was born in 1831 in what is now South Dakota. Sitting Bull showed great bravery and leadership skills, guiding his people during times of struggle and conflict.

As a warrior and chief, Sitting Bull fought to protect the land and way of life of his tribe. He was known for his wisdom, courage, and determination. Sitting Bull's name in the Lakota language is "Tatanka Iyotake," which means "Sitting Bull."

The author wrote this biography to inform readers about Sitting Bull's important role in history and to honor his contributions to Native American culture. By learning about Sitting Bull, readers can understand the strength and resilience of indigenous peoples.

Why do you think the author chose the word "fearless" to describe Sitting Bull?

_____

_____

How did Sitting Bull demonstrate his bravery and leadership skills?

_____

_____

Why is it important to learn about the contributions of historical figures like Sitting Bull?

_____

_____

Reading Skill: Compare and Contrast

Read the following texts:

George Washington

George Washington was the first President of the United States. He was born on February 22, 1732, in Virginia. Washington was a brave soldier who led the American Revolutionary War against the British. He played a crucial role in winning the war and gaining independence for the United States. As President, Washington helped create a strong and stable government and set important precedents for future leaders.

Abraham Lincoln

Abraham Lincoln was the 16th President of the United States. He was born on February 12, 1809, in Kentucky. Lincoln is best known for leading the country during the Civil War, a time when the United States was divided. He worked tirelessly to abolish slavery and keep the country united. Lincoln is also famous for delivering the Gettysburg Address, one of the most important speeches in American history.

What is one similarity between George Washington and Abraham Lincoln?

_____

_____

What is one difference between George Washington and Abraham Lincoln?

_____

_____

Why are both George Washington and Abraham Lincoln important figures in American history?

_____

_____

Biography 1: Martin Luther King, Jr.

Martin Luther King, Jr. was an important American civil rights leader whose activism was pivotal in the 1950s and 1960s. He was born on January 15, 1929, in Atlanta, Georgia. King grew up in a time when many people, especially Black people, were treated unfairly because of their skin color. He believed that all people should be treated equally, no matter their skin color. He gave speeches and organized peaceful protests to try to change the laws that discriminated against African Americans.

One of Martin Luther King, Jr.'s most famous speeches was called "I Have a Dream." In this speech, he talked about his dream that one day, people of all races would live together in peace and equality. He inspired many people with his words, and he worked hard to make his dream a reality.

For Fun! Take a coloring break!

I have a dream

Reading Comprehension Questions

Question 1: Who was Martin Luther King, Jr.?

_____

_____

Question 2: What did Martin Luther King, Jr. believe in?

_____

_____

Question 3: What did Martin Luther King, Jr. do to try to change the laws that discriminated against African Americans?

_____

_____

Question 4: Why is Martin Luther King, Jr. an important person in history?

_____

_____

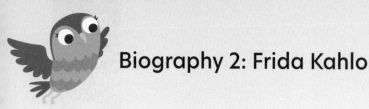

Biography 2: Frida Kahlo

Frida Kahlo was a Mexican artist who was born in 1907. She is known for her unique self-portraits and colorful paintings. Frida's artwork often reflects her life experiences, including her struggles with health issues and her love for her country. She used her art to express herself and share her story with the world.

Frida Kahlo was a woman who faced many challenges in her life, including a bus accident that left her with serious injuries. She spent months in bed recovering from her injuries, and it was during this time that she began to paint. Her artwork often features bright colors and bold patterns, and it is a reflection of her personal experiences and emotions.

For Fun! Grab a mirror and draw your self portrait!

Reading Comprehension Questions

Question 1: What is Frida Kahlo known for?

[ ] a. Playing soccer

[ ] b. Writing books

[ ] c. Painting self-portraits

[ ] d. Singing songs

Question 2: How did Frida Kahlo use her art?

[ ] a. To express herself and share her story

[ ] b. To make money

[ ] c. To show off her skills

[ ] d. To entertain people

Question 3: What challenges did Frida Kahlo face in her life?

[ ] a. She was rich and famous

[ ] b. She loved to travel

[ ] c. She had health issues and was injured in a bus accident

[ ] d. She was always happy

Question 4: Why is Frida Kahlo an important artist?

[ ] a. Because she loved to paint flowers

[ ] b. Because she was born in Mexico

[ ] c. Because she used her art to express herself and share her story

[ ] d. Because she only painted self-portraits

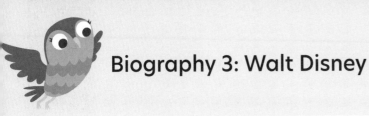

Biography 3: Walt Disney

RL.2.3
RL.2.7
RI.2.3
RI.2.8

Walt Disney was a famous American animator and entrepreneur. He created the character of Mickey Mouse, and his company produced many classic animated movies, such as Snow White and the Seven Dwarfs and Bambi. Disney's legacy also includes Disneyland and Disney World, two theme parks that attract visitors from around the world.

Disney's early life was not easy, as his family struggled financially. He had to work hard to pursue his dream of becoming an artist. Despite the challenges, he persevered, and his creativity and determination led him to great success.

Reading Comprehension Questions

Question 1: Who was Walt Disney?

_____

_____

_____

Question 2: What characters did Walt Disney create?

_____

_____

_____

Question 3: What is Walt Disney's legacy?

_____

_____

_____

Question 4: What challenges did Walt Disney face in his early life?

_____

_____

_____

For Fun! Color the castle!

⭐ **Definition**

Entrepreneur: a person who starts and runs a business

Biography 4: Albert Einstein

Albert Einstein is one of the most famous scientists in history. He was born in Germany in 1879 and grew up in a Jewish family. Einstein was a curious child who loved to explore the world around him. He was particularly interested in mathematics and physics, and he often spent hours tinkering with machines and conducting experiments.

Einstein is best known for his theory of relativity, which he published in 1905. This theory describes how time and space are linked, and it has had a profound impact on our understanding of the universe. Einstein also made many other important contributions to physics, including the discovery of the photoelectric effect and the development of the famous equation $E=mc^2$.

In addition to his scientific work, Einstein was also a committed pacifist and a vocal advocate for peace. He spoke out against war and violence, and he urged world leaders to work together to create a more peaceful world.

Reading Comprehension Questions

Question 1: Who was Albert Einstein?

[ ] a. A famous musician

[ ] b. A famous artist

[ ] c. A famous scientist

Question 2: What is Einstein best known for?

[ ] a. His theory of relativity

[ ] b. His discovery of electricity

[ ] c. His invention of the telephone

Question 3: What did Einstein discover in addition to his theory of relativity?

[ ] a. The photoelectric effect

[ ] b. The discovery of DNA

[ ] c. The development of the telephone

Question 4: What was Einstein's position on war and violence?

[ ] a. He supported war and violence

[ ] b. He was a committed pacifist and spoke out against war and violence

[ ] c. He was neutral on the issue of war and violence

★ **Definition**

Pacifist: a person who believes in the peaceful resolution of conflicts and opposes the use of violence or war to achieve their goals

$E=mc^2$

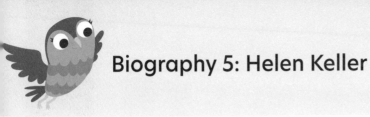

Biography 5: Helen Keller

RL.2.1
RL.2.2
RL.2.3
RL.2.4

Helen Keller was a remarkable woman who overcame great obstacles to become a leading advocate for people with disabilities. Keller was born in Alabama in 1880 and lost both her sight and hearing after a severe illness at the age of 19 months.

Despite her challenges, Keller learned to communicate using sign language and Braille, and went on to graduate from college and become an author and lecturer. She was also a champion for women's suffrage and advocated for workers' rights.

Reading Comprehension Questions

Question 1: What obstacles did Helen Keller overcome?

_____

_____

Question 2: How did Helen Keller communicate with others?

_____

_____

Question 3: What were some of the things Helen Keller accomplished in her life?

_____

_____

Question 4: Why is Helen Keller considered a remarkable woman?

_____

_____

Biography 6: Simone Biles

Simone Biles is an American gymnast who is widely regarded as one of the greatest athletes of all time. Born in Columbus, Ohio in 1997, Biles began practicing gymnastics at a young age. She quickly demonstrated her talent for the sport, and by the time she was a teenager, she was competing at the highest levels.

Biles made her debut at the Olympic Games in 2016, where she won four gold medals and one bronze. She also became the first female gymnast to win three consecutive world all-around titles. In addition to her impressive athletic achievements, Biles has been an outspoken advocate for mental health awareness and has used her platform to promote positive change in the world.

In 2021, Biles made headlines when she withdrew from several events at the Olympic Games in Tokyo, citing concerns about her mental health. Despite the criticism she faced from some quarters, Biles received widespread support and admiration for her decision to prioritize her well-being.

Reading Comprehension Questions

Question 1: Who is Simone Biles?

[ ] a. An American soccer player

[ ] b. An American gymnast

[ ] c. An American swimmer

Question 2: When did Simone Biles make her debut at the Olympic Games?

[ ] a. 2008

[ ] b. 2012

[ ] c. 2016

Question 3: What is Simone Biles known for besides her athletic achievements?

[ ] a. Advocacy for mental health awareness

[ ] b. Political activism

[ ] c. Business entrepreneurship

Question 4: Why did Simone Biles withdraw from several events at the Olympic Games in 2021?

[ ] a. She was injured

[ ] b. She was tired

[ ] c. She was concerned about her mental health

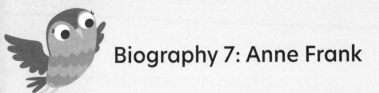

Biography 7: Anne Frank

Anne Frank was a young Jewish girl who lived in Amsterdam during World War II. When the Nazis began persecuting Jews, Anne's family went into hiding in a secret annex behind her father's business. Anne wrote about her experiences in a diary, which has become famous around the world.

While in hiding, Anne wrote about her hopes, fears, and dreams. She also wrote about the difficulties of living in such a small space with her family and others in hiding. Sadly, Anne and her family were eventually discovered and sent to concentration camps. Anne died of typhus at the age of 15, but her diary has become a symbol of hope and resilience.

For Fun! Decorate your own diary!

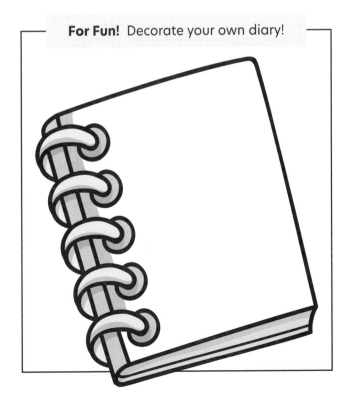

Reading Comprehension Questions

Question 1: Who was Anne Frank?

_____

_____

_____

Question 2: Where did Anne Frank and her family go into hiding?

_____

_____

_____

Question 3: Why did Anne Frank write in a diary?

_____

_____

_____

Question 4: Why is Anne Frank's diary important?

_____

_____

_____

Biography 8: Malala Yousafzai

RI.2.1
RI.2.3
RI.2.4

Malala Yousafzai is a young woman who has become famous for her advocacy for girls' education. She was born in Pakistan in 1997, and she grew up in a region called Swat Valley. When the Taliban took control of the area, they did not allow girls to go to school. Malala refused to accept this, and she spoke out against the Taliban's policies.

Malala became a well-known activist at a young age. She gave speeches and interviews in which she talked about the importance of education for all children, especially girls. She also started a blog under a pretend name, which chronicled her experiences living under Taliban rule.

In 2012, Malala was shot by a member of the Taliban while she was on her way to school. She survived the attack, and she has continued to speak out for education and human rights. In recognition of her activism, she was awarded the Nobel Peace Prize in 2014.

For Fun! Search for the following words:

MALALA

SCHOOL

GIRLS

BLOG

R	C	S	I	G	V
M	A	L	A	L	A
A	U	R	Y	R	W
P	E	I	H	U	C
Q	B	G	O	L	B
L	O	O	H	C	S

Reading Comprehension Questions

Question 1: What is Malala famous for advocating for?

[ ] a. Boys' education

[ ] b. Girls' education

[ ] c. No education

[ ] d. Education for only certain children

Question 2: Where was Malala born?

[ ] a. Pakistan

[ ] b. India

[ ] c. Afghanistan

[ ] d. Iraq

Question 3: What did Malala start under a pseudonym?

[ ] a. A newspaper

[ ] b. A book club

[ ] c. A blog

[ ] d. A podcast

Question 4: What happened to Malala in 2012?

[ ] a. She won a Nobel Peace Prize

[ ] b. She gave a speech about girls' education

[ ] c. She was shot by the Taliban

[ ] d. She started a school for girls

⭐ **Definition**

Advocacy: the act of publicly supporting or recommending a particular cause or policy

Biography 9: Abraham Lincoln

Abraham Lincoln is one of the most well-known and beloved presidents in the history of the United States. He was born on February 12, 1809 in a log cabin in Kentucky and grew up in poverty. Despite his humble beginnings, Lincoln was a gifted student and a great public speaker. He used his talents to become a lawyer and then a politician.

Lincoln's presidency was marked by many important events. Perhaps the most significant was the Civil War. This war pitted the North against the South, and it was fought over the issue of slavery. Lincoln was firmly opposed to slavery, and he believed that the Union needed to be preserved at all costs. He worked tirelessly to rally support for the Union cause, and he ultimately led the North to victory.

Another important event during Lincoln's presidency was the Emancipation Proclamation. This document declared that all slaves in the Confederate states were to be set free. This was a major turning point in the war, as it meant that the Union was fighting not just to preserve the nation, but also to end slavery. The Emancipation Proclamation is still considered one of the most important documents in American history.

Sadly, Lincoln's presidency was cut short by his assassination. He was shot by a man named John Wilkes Booth while attending a play at Ford's Theatre in Washington, D.C. Lincoln died the next day, leaving behind a nation in mourning.

★ Definition
Mourning: the expression of deep sadness, usually as a result of the loss of a loved one

Reading Comprehension Questions

Question 1: Where was Abraham Lincoln born?

[ ] a. In a log cabin

[ ] b. In a mansion

[ ] c. In a castle

[ ] d. In a skyscraper

Question 2: What was the Civil War fought over?

[ ] a. Taxes

[ ] b. Slavery

[ ] c. Land rights

[ ] d. Religion

Question 3: What is the Emancipation Proclamation?

[ ] a. A document that ended slavery in the United States

[ ] b. A document that declared war on England

[ ] c. A document that declared independence from Great Britain

[ ] d. A document that established the United States Constitution

Question 4: How did Abraham Lincoln die?

[ ] a. He died of natural causes

[ ] b. He was shot by John Wilkes Booth

[ ] c. He died in a plane crash

[ ] d. He was drowned

Biography 10: Neil Armstrong

Neil Armstrong was an American astronaut and the first human being to set foot on the moon. Born in Wapakoneta, Ohio in 1930, Armstrong became interested in aviation at an early age. He earned his pilot's license before he was old enough to drive a car and served as a naval aviator before joining NASA in 1962.

Armstrong made history on July 20, 1969, when he and fellow astronaut Edwin "Buzz" Aldrin landed the Apollo 11 lunar module on the moon's surface. Armstrong famously uttered the words "That's one small step for man, one giant leap for mankind," as he took his first steps on the moon's surface.

After his historic moonwalk, Armstrong returned to Earth and continued to work for NASA. He retired from the space agency in 1971 and became a professor of engineering at the University of Cincinnati. He died in 2012 at the age of 82.

Reading Comprehension Questions

Question 1: Who was Neil Armstrong?

_____

_____

Question 2: What did Neil Armstrong say when he took his first steps on the moon's surface?

_____

_____

Question 3: What did Neil Armstrong do after he retired from NASA?

_____

_____

Question 4: When did Neil Armstrong die?

_____

_____

Section 4

POEMS

A poem is a type of literary work that uses language to create an emotional or imaginative experience for the reader. Poems often use literary devices such as rhyme, rhythm, repetition, and figurative language to convey meaning and create a unique reading experience.

Reading and writing poetry can help students improve their vocabulary, phonemic awareness, and language comprehension skills. Additionally, poetry can be a fun and engaging way to introduce students to different cultures, perspectives, and emotions.

The study of poetry is an important part of the second grade reading comprehension curriculum as it helps students develop their language skills, broaden their perspectives, and cultivate a love for literature.

Reading Skills

Before you jump into the full stories in this section, brush up on your reading skills with the activities on the following pages.

 Reading the Poem Multiple Times

 Identify the Main Idea

 Compare and Contrast

 Analyze the Language

Come back to this page and color in the stars after you finish each activity!

Reading Skill: Read the Poem Multiple Times

Frozen Delight

In a world of frozen delight,
Ice cream brings smiles, oh so bright.
Scoops on cones, flavors galore,
Taste the sweetness, want some more?

Chocolate, vanilla, swirls of delight,
A treat that makes our hearts take flight.
Creamy, cold, and oh so sweet,
A frozen dessert that can't be beat.

1. *Read the poem silently.*
2. *Read the poem out loud.*
3. *Write two lines of the poem that you want to memorize:*

_____

_____

☆ Reading Skill: Identify the Main Idea

Read the following poem:

Reach for the Sky

On snowy slopes, with board in hand,
We glide across a wintry land.
Snowboarding is our favorite ride,
With every turn, we feel the pride.

We slide down hills, so fast and free,
Our hearts filled with pure glee.
Jumping high, up in the air,
Feeling weightless, without a care.

The wind in our face, the thrill so real,
Snowboarding gives us an incredible feel.
With every trick and flip we try,
We challenge ourselves, reaching the sky.

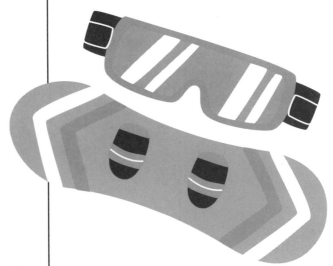

What is the main idea of the poem?

_____

What is the author trying to convey about snowboarding?

_____

How does the author describe the feeling of snowboarding?

_____

What are some ideas mentioned in the poem that make snowboarding exciting?

_____

Reading Skill: Compare and Contrast

Play Ball!

In the summer sun, on the green field,

With gloves and bats, our team will wield.

We throw, we catch, we run the bases,

In this game, we find our happy places.

The pitcher winds up, the ball is thrown,

We swing our bats, with hopes high-flown.

With each crack of the bat,
we aim for a hit,

Running the bases, never ready to quit.

The crowd cheers loud, as
we steal the base,

A home run, a victory, our hearts race.

Baseball is a game of teamwork and fun,

Playing under the warm and shining sun.

Touchdown!

On the field, in helmets and pads,

We charge forward, feeling strong and glad.

Running, passing, tackling with might,

In this game, for every yard we fight.

The quarterback shouts the play,

We follow his lead, no time to delay.

We dodge defenders, we push through,

With teamwork and skill, the end zone in view.

The crowd roars with excitement and cheer,

Touchdowns and field goals, victory is near.

Football is a game of strength and speed,

A team sport where we work
together to succeed.

How are the themes of teamwork and competition portrayed in the poems about baseball and football?

_____

_____

Compare the tone or feeling of the baseball poem with the tone or feeling of the football poem. How are they similar or different?

_____

_____

☆ Reading Skill: Analyze the Language

Groove and Glide: The Breakdancing Lizard

In a groovy land where lizards reside,
A breakdancing lizard took us for a ride.
With scales that shimmered, vibrant and bright,
He moved to the beat, a stunning sight.

His spins were as swift as a whirlwind's might,
As he rocked to the rhythm, dancing with delight.
His body twisted and turned like a snake,
Intricate moves he would flawlessly make.

The lizard's tail whipped, it popped and locked,
His feet stomped the ground, his body rocked.
With flips and freezes, he stole the show,
A breakdancing lizard, full of glow.

A **simile** is a figure of speech that compares two things using the words "like" or "as." It is used to create a vivid image or enhance the meaning of a statement.

Identify a simile in the poem and explain what it means.

_____

How would you describe the lizard's dancing style?

_____

What are some key actions and movements described in the poem?

_____

How does the poet create a sense of excitement in the poem?

_____

Poem 1: Stinky Feet

My feet are oh so stinky,

It makes me want to cry,

I try to wash them every day,

But the smell won't say goodbye.

My mom says to wear
clean socks,

And shoes that let them breathe,

But even with these helpful tips,

My feet still smell like cheese.

Here's a tip!

To understand a poet's tone, pay attention to the words and phrases they use. If the words sound happy, sad, or excited, it can give clues about the tone of the poem. Also, think about how the poem makes you feel. Does it make you feel joyful, thoughtful, or maybe even scared? These feelings can help you understand the tone of the poem better.

Reading Comprehension Questions

Question 1: What is the speaker's problem in the poem?

_____

_____

_____

Question 2: What does the speaker's mom suggest to help with the problem?

_____

_____

_____

Question 3: Do the tips from the speaker's mom solve the problem?

_____

_____

_____

Question 4: What is the speaker's tone in the poem?

_____

_____

_____

Poem 2: Lunchtime

At school, at noon,
we all go to eat,

A break from the day and
a chance to meet,

With friends we chat
and laugh and play,

And fuel our bodies for
the rest of the day.

We bring our lunch or
get it at school,

So many choices, it's
hard to choose,

A sandwich, an apple,
or maybe some chips,

We can even get a drink
with a straw that flips.

Reading Comprehension Questions

Question 1: What is the poem about?

[ ] a. Lunch at school

[ ] b. Breakfast at home

[ ] c. Dinner with family

[ ] d. Going to the movies

Question 2: What do the students do during lunchtime?

[ ] a. Play games

[ ] b. Read books

[ ] c. Chat with friends

[ ] d. Take a nap

Question 3: What kind of food do students eat during lunchtime?

[ ] a. Ice cream

[ ] b. Cake

[ ] c. Sandwich, apple, or chips

[ ] d. Pizza

Question 4: What is the purpose of lunchtime at school?

[ ] a. To take a nap

[ ] b. To have fun

[ ] c. To meet friends

[ ] d. To fuel our bodies for
the rest of the day

Poem 3: The Duck Who Couldn't Swim

There was a little duckling
Who lived by the pond so blue,
But unlike all the other ducks,
This one couldn't swim, it's true.

He tried to paddle with his feet,
And flap his wings so fast,
But every time he hit the water,
He sank down to the bottom, aghast.

The other ducks would swim around,
And quack with glee and pride,
While the little duckling stood alone,
On the shore, trying not to hide.

One day a friendly frog appeared,
And asked why he looked so sad,
The little duckling explained his plight,
And the frog was quite glad.

He showed him how to kick his feet,
And keep his wings tucked tight,
And before too long, the little duckling,
Was paddling with all his might.

Now he swims with all his friends,
And quacks with joy and glee,
Thanks to the friendly frog's help,
He's happy as can be.

Reading Comprehension Questions

Question 1: What was different about the little duckling?

_____

_____

_____

Question 2: What did the other ducks do that made the little duckling feel sad?

_____

_____

_____

Question 3: Who helped the little duckling learn how to swim?

_____

_____

_____

Question 4: How did the little duckling feel after he learned how to swim?

_____

_____

_____

Poem 4: The Science Fair

In the science fair, we all compete

To show what we've
learned, it's quite a feat

We've made volcanoes,
robots, and more

And explained the science
behind the roar

There are displays on tables galore

The judges come by to explore

Asking questions about our creations

We answer with pride and elation

Ribbons are given out at the end

To those who have shown
their science trend

First place, second, and
third are found

We all cheer, with applause
that resounds

For Fun! Draw a picture of the story.

Reading Comprehension Questions

Question 1: What is a science fair?

_____

_____

_____

Question 2: What do people
make for a science fair?

_____

_____

_____

Question 3: What happens
when the judges come by?

_____

_____

_____

Question 4: What do people receive
at the end of a science fair?

_____

_____

_____

Poem 5: An Overflowing Piggy Bank

My piggy bank is
filled with coins,

It's bursting at the seams,

I've saved up every penny,

And it's overflowing with gleams.

I shake it and it rattles,

With every coin inside,

The jingle and the jangle,

Makes me feel so satisfied.

I know I can buy something,

But I'm not sure what to get,

I'll keep on saving up my coins,

And wait for something
I can't forget.

Reading Comprehension Questions

Question 1: What is the poem about?

_____

_____

_____

Question 2: What does the speaker
do with their piggy bank?

_____

_____

_____

Question 3: Why does the
speaker feel satisfied?

_____

_____

_____

Question 4: What does the speaker
plan to do with their coins?

_____

_____

_____

Section 5

MASTERY

Now that you've learned foundational reading comprehension skills for many different kinds of texts, and practiced how to get the most understanding from each one, it's time to show everyone how much you've learned! Take a swing at the following activities and give yourself a huge high five for the phenomenal work you've done. Ask your caregiver to help you share your activities with the team at Modern Kid Press for an opportunity to win special prizes and be featured on our website and in future books! (Parents: flip to the back of the book for more information.)

Activities

 Create a Comic Strip   Create a Puppet Show

 Design a Board Game   Make a Movie Trailer

 Write a Letter

Come back to this page and color in the stars after you finish each activity!

Read the following story:

The Unmeltable Ice Cream Sandwiches

Once upon a time, in a magical ice cream factory, there were ice cream sandwiches that couldn't melt. Yes, you heard it right! These ice cream sandwiches had a special power that kept them frozen no matter how hot the sun shone.

In the town of Frostville, where the ice cream factory was located, the children couldn't believe their luck. They could enjoy their ice cream sandwiches without worrying about them turning into sticky puddles. It was a dream come true!

One sunny summer day, a group of friends named Max, Lily, and Sam decided to put the unmeltable ice cream sandwiches to the test. They took their ice cream sandwiches out for a picnic in the park. The sun was scorching, but their treats remained cool and delicious.

As they sat on a blanket, they noticed curious animals approaching them. A mischievous squirrel named Nutty wanted a taste of the magical ice cream sandwich. But as soon as Nutty took a bite, it felt a frosty chill in its tiny teeth. Startled, the squirrel ran away in surprise.

Max, Lily, and Sam couldn't stop giggling. They realized that their ice cream sandwiches were so cold that even animals couldn't handle them. It was like having a superpower!

Word about the unmeltable ice cream sandwiches spread quickly, and soon, children from all over the town flocked to the factory to get their hands on these extraordinary treats. The factory worked day and night to produce enough ice cream sandwiches for everyone.

As time went on, the ice cream factory became a popular tourist spot. People traveled from far and wide just to see the incredible unmeltable ice cream sandwiches and taste their frosty goodness.

And so, the legend of the unmeltable ice cream sandwiches lived on in Frostville. Whenever the sun shone brightly, children would gather with their friends and enjoy the magical treats that brought smiles and laughter to everyone's faces.

Onomatopoeia is a literary device used in writing and poetry where a word is used to imitate or recreate the sound of something. Some examples are "buzz," "hiss," and "meow!"

Create a comic strip based on the story "The Unmeltable Ice Cream Sandwiches." Use speech bubbles, thought bubbles, and onomatopoeia to convey the characters' thoughts, feelings, and actions.

Activity 2: Design a Board Game

Read the following story:

The Quest for Unity

Once in an enchanted forest, four talking animals embarked on a quest for a magical pot. Oliver the owl, Bella the bunny, Milo the monkey, and Luna the lioness encountered helpful creatures and faced obstacles. With their combined skills and determination, they outsmarted a cunning fox named Felix and obtained the pot. Instead of seeking personal gain, they wished for unity and harmony in the forest. The pot fulfilled their selfless desire, and the forest thrived. The friends became heroes, spreading kindness in their adventures and always supporting each other.

Design your board game on the next page!

1. Design a colorful game board that represents the magical land in "The Quest for Unity." Include different terrains, landmarks, and obstacles that the adventurers may encounter on their journey.

2. Divide the board into spaces or sections to create a path for the players to follow. Draw or decorate each space to match the story's elements.

3. Add start and finish points to the board, indicating where the adventurers begin their race and where the treasure is hidden.

4. Create character tokens.

5. Create game rules. Write them on the back of the game board.

_____

Title

Start

Finish

Design and cut out your player tokens:

Game Rules

RULE 1: ____________________

RULE 2: ____________________

RULE 3: ____________________

RULE 4: ____________________

RULE 5: ____________________

Activity 3: Write a Letter

Read the following story:

Zara's Interplanetary Adventure: Exploring Earth's Wonders

In a distant galaxy, on the planet Zog, there lived a curious second-grade alien named Zara. Zara was fascinated by humans on Earth and loved learning about their world. She decided to visit Earth to see everything for herself. Landing in a park, she observed children playing and saw the joy they shared. Exploring a city, she discovered the bustling life and delicious food. Zara met kind people who taught her about science, art, teaching, and helping others. When she returned to Zog, Zara shared her adventure, inspiring her friends to learn more about Earth. Together, they formed a club to explore and celebrate Earth's wonders. Zara became a bridge between two worlds, connecting Zog and Earth.

Write a letter to Zara.

Ask questions, offer advice, or share your thoughts and feelings about the character and the story.

Activity 4: Create a Puppet Show

Rosie and Max's Brave Adventure

Rosie and Max were the best of friends, a rabbit and a dog who lived in a cozy neighborhood. But they had one problem - they were scared of their own shadows! Whenever the sun was out, their shadows made them feel afraid.

One day, they decided to face their fear. They sat together and talked about their feelings. Then, they practiced standing still and watching their shadows. They realized that shadows moved and changed shape. They even played games with their shadows and had fun.

As time passed, Rosie and Max grew braver. They learned that shadows were nothing to be afraid of. They embraced their shadows and enjoyed the different shapes they made.

From that day on, Rosie and Max were no longer scared. They knew that facing their fears together made them stronger. They continued their adventures, knowing that their shadows were just a part of who they were.

Supplies Needed:

- Socks or gloves
- Markers, crayons, or colored pencils
- Craft paper or construction paper
- Scissors
- Glue or tape
- Popsicle sticks or straws
- Optional: Buttons, yarn, fabric scraps for additional puppet decorations

Instructions:

1. Design and Decorate Puppets: Use markers, crayons, or colored pencils to draw the faces and features of Rosie and Max on the sock or glove puppets. You can also cut out craft paper or construction paper to create ears, noses, or other accessories for the puppets. Get creative and make them as colorful as you'd like!

2. Set the Stage: Find a space in your house where you can set up your puppet show stage. You can use a table, a box, or even a blanket stretched between two chairs. Make sure it's a comfortable and well-lit area.

3. Create Backgrounds: Use craft paper, construction paper, or even drawings to create backgrounds for your puppet show. For example, you can draw a scene with trees and a bright sky to represent the outdoors where Rosie and Max discover their shadows.

4. Practice Dialogue: Decide on the dialogue for your puppet show. Use the story as a reference, and have fun adding your own lines for the characters. Practice speaking in different voices to make the puppets come to life!

5. Perform Your Puppet Show: Gather your family or friends as your audience, and put on your puppet show! Use the puppets to act out the story of Rosie and Max's adventure and how they bravely faced their fear of shadows. Remember to move the puppets around, use different expressions, and bring your story to life.

Activity 5: Make a Movie Trailer

The Laughing Pirate's Surprise

Once upon a time, there was a silly pirate named Captain Chuckles. He couldn't stop laughing, which made his crew laugh too. One day, while sailing the high seas, they encountered a fierce storm. The winds howled, and the waves crashed against their ship. Captain Chuckles tried to steer the ship, but his constant laughter made it difficult for him to focus.

As the storm raged on, a gigantic sea serpent emerged from the depths. It had sharp teeth and a menacing gaze. The crew panicked, but Captain Chuckles couldn't help himself – he burst into laughter at the sight of the sea serpent. The crew urged him to be serious and help them face the danger.

With great effort, Captain Chuckles managed to control his laughter and think quickly. He devised a plan to distract the sea serpent by telling it silly jokes and making funny faces. As he entertained the sea serpent, the crew managed to navigate their ship away from the dangerous creature.

Once the storm subsided and the sea serpent disappeared, Captain Chuckles and his crew celebrated their victory. They realized that Captain Chuckles' laughter could be both a challenge and a strength. From that day on, they embraced their silly nature, using laughter to overcome obstacles and bring joy to their adventures on the high seas.

Supplies Needed:

- Smartphone or tablet with a camera
- Props and costumes (use household items)
- Paper or poster board
- Markers or colored pencils

Steps:

1. Read "The Laughing Pirate's Surprise."

2. Write a short script with the most exciting parts of the story.

3. Create simple props and costumes using things around the house.

4. Find locations at home or in the backyard to film.

5. Set up your camera and record scenes following your script.

6. Use household items for special effects (e.g., flashlights for lighting).

7. Edit your footage on a smartphone or tablet.

8. Make a movie trailer poster or title card on paper.

9. Share your movie trailer with family and friends.

Tips:

- Keep the script exciting and to the point.

- Use strong action words and descriptive language.

- Practice reading the script aloud.

- Have fun and bring the story to life!

SECOND GRADE READING: LITERATURE STANDARDS

Key Ideas and Details

RL.2.1. Ask and answer such questions as who, what, where, when, why, and how to demonstrate understanding of key details in a text.

RL.2.2. Recount stories, including fables and folktales from diverse cultures, and determine their central message, lesson, or moral.

RL.2.3. Describe how characters in a story respond to major events and challenges.

Craft and Structure

RL.2.4. Describe how words and phrases (e.g., regular beats, alliteration, rhymes, repeated lines) supply rhythm and meaning in a story, poem, or song.

RL.2.5. Describe the overall structure of a story, including describing how the beginning introduces the story and the ending concludes the action.

RL.2.6. Acknowledge differences in the points of view of characters, including by speaking in a different voice for each character when reading dialogue aloud.

Integration of Knowledge and Ideas

RL.2.7. Use information gained from the illustrations and words in a print or digital text to demonstrate understanding of its characters, setting, or plot.

RL.2.8. (Not applicable to literature)

RL.2.9. Compare and contrast two or more versions of the same story (e.g., Cinderella stories) by different authors or from different cultures.

Range of Reading and Level of Text Complexity

RL.2.10. By the end of the year, read and comprehend literature, including stories and poetry, in the grades 2-3 text complexity band proficiently, with scaffolding as needed at the high end of the range.

SECOND GRADE READING: INFORMATIONAL TEXT STANDARDS

Key Ideas and Details

RI.2.1. Ask and answer such questions as who, what, where, when, why, and how to demonstrate understanding of key details in a text.

RI.2.2. Identify the main topic of a multiparagraph text as well as the focus of specific paragraphs within the text.

RI.2.3. Describe the connection between a series of historical events, scientific ideas or concepts, or steps in technical procedures in a text.

Craft and Structure

RI.2.4. Determine the meaning of words and phrases in a text relevant to a grade 2 topic or subject area.

RI.2.5. Know and use various text features (e.g., captions, bold print, subheadings, glossaries, indexes, electronic menus, icons) to locate key facts or information in a text efficiently.

RI.2.6. Identify the main purpose of a text, including what the author wants to answer, explain, or describe.

Integration of Knowledge and Ideas

RI.2.7. Explain how specific images (e.g., a diagram showing how a machine works) contribute to and clarify a text.

RI.2.8. Describe how reasons support specific points the author makes in a text.

RI.2.9. Compare and contrast the most important points presented by two texts on the same topic.

Range of Reading and Level of Text Complexity

RI.2.10. By the end of year, read and comprehend informational texts, including history/social studies, science, and technical texts, in the grades 2-3 text complexity band proficiently, with scaffolding as needed at the high end of the range.

ANSWER KEY

Section 1: Literary Texts

Story 1: Baylee and Jude's Magical Discovery
1. A
2. C
3. B
4. A

Story 2: Rufus's Special Friend
1. B
2. C
3. B
4. C

Story 3: A Very Musical Unicorn
1. Twinkle met a rabbit who played the saxophone, that encouraged her to keep practicing.
2. Twinkle practiced every day with the rabbit's guidance to become better at playing the saxophone.
3. Twinkle's friends were amazed by her talent and performances.
4. Twinkle was hesitant to continue playing the saxophone at first because she found it challenging to play with her hooves.

Story 4: Bubbles' Grand Adventure
1. The name of the ticklish water bottle in the story is Bubbles.
2. It was difficult for Bubbles' friends to take her out of the fridge because she would giggle uncontrollably whenever she was touched or bumped into.
3. The carton of milk suggested that they roll Bubbles out of the fridge slowly and carefully, so she wouldn't get too ticklish and start giggling.
4. No, Bubbles was no longer afraid of leaving the fridge after her adventure with her friends.

The answers to the word puzzle are:
BUBBLES
TOASTER
BOTTLE
FRIDGE

Story 5: Fish Need Friends, Too
1. Goldie had trouble with feeling lonely because she didn't have any fish friends.
2. Fred and Goldie played a game where they would swim through the plastic plants together.
3. Goldie felt a little left out when the little girl's friends came over.
4. Goldie made the little girl's friends laugh by swimming back and forth in front of the glass, making silly faces and wiggling her tail.

Story 6: Hank's Big Idea
1. A
2. A
3. A
4. C

Story 7: Animal Parade
1. D
2. A
3. C
4. C

Story 8: Alien Food Fight
1. The aliens were having a space picnic.
2. The blue alien felt sad because she didn't like to waste food.
3. The blue alien talked to the other aliens and explained why it was important to respect food.
4. The aliens decided to stop the food fight and share their space snacks instead.

Story 9: The Secret Life of Toys
1. The toys come to life and have adventures.
2. The other toys are hesitant to accept him at first.
3. The toys get some snacks.
4. The toys freeze to pretend to be just regular toys again.

Story 10: Samantha's Silly Word Problem
1. Samantha loved to play with words.
2. The silly word Samantha discovered that made her giggle was "flibbertigibbet."
3. Samantha got in trouble when she said silly words during class.

4. Samantha realized she needed to control her love for silly words because she was getting in trouble for saying them too much.

Story 11: The Wizard's Special Day

1. The wizard went to the amusement park to have fun while testing his magic.
2. The wizard used his wand to make himself invisible.
3. The wizard pointed his wand at the ride and muttered a spell, and the teddy bear appeared next to the little girl.
4. The wizard will not be invisible the next time he visits the amusement park.

Story 12: The Silliest Story in the World

1. The cow tickled the farmer.
2. They thought the farm was a new kind of amusement park.
3. They convinced the aliens to stay on the farm forever and ride them like carnival rides every day.
4. Sam.

Story 13: Magnolia the Explorer

1. B
2. C
3. C
4. A

Story 14: Penelope's Big Surprise

1. B
2. A
3. B
4. C

Story 15: Howling for Speed

1. B
2. D
3. B
4. C

Section 2: Informational Texts

Information 1: The History of Television

1. The original purpose of television was to show moving pictures.
2. The first television sets were black and white, and the screens were small.
3. People watched silly and fun shows, as well as educational shows, on television in the 1950s.
4. Today, we have color TVs, flat screens, and even streaming services.

Information 2: Space Exploration

1. A
2. D
3. A
4. C

Information 3: What Makes Airplanes Fly?

1. The way airplanes use their wings to create lift is the key to flight for airplanes.
2. The shape of an airplane's wings is curved on the top and flat on the bottom.
3. Thrust is created by the airplane's engines, which push the airplane through the air.
4. An airplane can control its direction and altitude using its tail and flaps.

Information 4: How Human Brains Work

1. The cells in the brain are called Neurons.
2. Neurons communicate with each other through electrical and chemical signals.
3. The occipital lobe is responsible for processing visual information.
4. Rest and sleep are important for the brain to function properly.

Information 5: All About Carpentry

1. Carpentry is the art and science of working with wood to create beautiful and functional objects.
2. Carpenters use a variety of tools, such as hammers, saws, chisels, and drills, to cut, shape, and join pieces of wood.

3. Measuring accurately is important in carpentry to ensure that pieces of wood fit together properly and the finished product looks and functions as intended.
4. One way carpenters join pieces of wood together is using nails, screws, glue, or dovetail joints.

Information 6: The First Zoo
1. The first zoo was located in a temple in the city of Hierakonpolis in Egypt.
2. The first zoo housed many different animals, including elephants, lions, baboons, and even a hippopotamus.
3. The House of Anubis was not just a place to display animals. It was also a religious center where people came to worship the gods.
4. Some people argue that zoos are necessary for conservation and education, while others believe that they are cruel and unnecessary.

Information 7: How Crayons Are Made
1. B
2. C
3. C
4. A

Information 8: The Perfect Pancake Recipe
1. B
2. A
3. C
4. D

Information 9: Weird Weather
1. B
2. B
3. A
4. A

Information 10: The Life Cycle of Plants
1. A
2. A
3. C
4. A

Information 11: Magnets Are Amazing!
1. Magnets work by creating a magnetic field that pulls on other magnetic materials. Inside a magnet, there are small particles called electrons that spin in the same direction, creating a magnetic field around the magnet.
2. The strongest part of a magnet is the ends or poles, which are called the North and South poles.
3. When opposite poles of two magnets are brought near each other, they attract each other.
4. Magnets are used in many different ways, including holding notes on a refrigerator, powering machines in factories, and in compasses.

Information 12: All About Volcanoes
1. B
2. C
3. B
4. A

Information 13: The History of Theater
1. People in ancient Greece gathered in outdoor amphitheaters to watch plays and performances.
2. Ancient Greek plays often told stories about gods and goddesses.
3. William Shakespeare became one of the most famous playwrights in history in the 16th century.
4. People can watch plays and musicals in theaters, as well as on television and online.

Information 14: All About Skyscrapers
1. Skyscrapers are tall buildings that can be found in many cities around the world.
2. Skyscrapers are built with strong materials such as steel and concrete.
3. The first skyscraper was the Home Insurance Building, built in Chicago in 1885.
4. Answer4 : The Burj Khalifa in Dubai is currently the tallest skyscraper in the world, measuring over 828 meters (2,716 feet) tall.

Information 15: Soccer!
1. B
2. C
3. B
4. A

Section 3: Biographical Texts

Biography 1: Martin Luther King, Jr.
1. Martin Luther King, Jr. was an important American civil rights leader whose activism was pivotal in the 1950s and 1960s.
2. Martin Luther King, Jr. believed that all people should be treated equally, no matter their skin color.
3. Martin Luther King, Jr. gave speeches and organized peaceful protests to try to change the laws that discriminated against African Americans.
4. Martin Luther King, Jr. is an important person in history because he fought for civil rights and equality for all people, especially African Americans. He used his words and actions to inspire change and make a difference in the world.

Biography 2: Frida Kahlo
1. C
2. A
3. C
4. C

Biography 3: Walt Disney
1. Walt Disney was a famous American animator and entrepreneur.
2. Walt Disney created the character of Mickey Mouse.
3. Walt Disney's legacy includes Disneyland and Disney World, two theme parks that attract visitors from around the world.
4. Walt Disney's family struggled financially, which made it difficult for him to pursue his dream of becoming an artist.

Biography 4: Albert Einstein
1. C
2. A
3. A
4. B

Biography 5: Helen Keller
1. Helen Keller overcame the obstacles of being both blind and deaf after a severe illness at 19 months old.
2. Helen Keller communicated with others using sign language and Braille.
3. Helen Keller graduated from college, became an author and lecturer, and was a champion for women's suffrage and workers' rights.
4. Helen Keller is considered a remarkable woman because she overcame great obstacles to become a leading advocate for people with disabilities, and she accomplished many important things in her life despite her challenges.

Biography 6: Simone Biles
1. B
2. C
3. A
4. C

Biography 7: Anne Frank
1. Anne Frank was a young Jewish girl who lived in Amsterdam during World War II.
2. Anne Frank and her family went into hiding in a secret annex behind her father's business.
3. Anne Frank wrote in a diary to express her hopes, fears, dreams, and the difficulties of living in hiding.
4. Anne Frank's diary is important because it has become a symbol of hope and resilience, and provides a firsthand account of the experiences of Jews during the Holocaust.

Biography 8: Malala Yousafzai
1. B
2. A
3. C
4. C

Biography 9: Abraham Lincoln
1. A
2. B
3. A
4. B

Biography 10: Neil Armstrong
1. Neil Armstrong was an American astronaut and the first human being to set foot on the moon.
2. Neil Armstrong famously uttered the words "That's one small step for man, one giant leap for mankind."
3. After he retired from NASA, Neil Armstrong became a professor of engineering at the University of Cincinnati.
4. Neil Armstrong died in 2012 at the age of 82.

Section 4: Poems

Poem 1: Stinky Feet
1. The speaker's problem is that their feet smell bad.
2. The speaker's mom suggests wearing clean socks and shoes that let their feet breathe.
3. No, the tips do not solve the problem.
4. The speaker's tone is sad and frustrated.

Poem 2: Lunchtime
1. A
2. C
3. C
4. D

Poem 3: The Duck Who Couldn't Swim
1. The little duckling couldn't swim.
2. The other ducks swam around and quacked with glee and pride.
3. The friendly frog.
4. The little duckling was happy as can be.

Poem 4: The Science Fair
1. A science fair is an event where people compete by showing what they have learned through their scientific projects.
2. People make projects such as volcanoes, robots, and other creations to explain the science behind them.
3. The judges come by to explore and ask questions about the scientific creations on display.
4. People receive ribbons, such as first place, second place, and third place, to show how well they did in the science fair.

Poem 5: An Overflowing Piggy Bank
1. The poem is about a piggy bank that is overflowing with coins.
2. The speaker shakes their piggy bank and listens to the sound of the coins.
3. The speaker feels satisfied because they have saved up every penny and their piggy bank is overflowing with coins.
4. The speaker plans to keep on saving up their coins until they find something they can't forget.

Kids Teach Kids

Hey parents! We love seeing your kid's awesome work!
Email samples and videos of your kids explaining their creations to

modernkidpress@gmail.com

with the subject line

"Kids Teach Kids: Reading Grade 2"

and we'll send some your goodies your way!